Joe,

I hope you (and) that this brings value to you. My goal is to bring clarity to this discussion so that we can achieve that end that we so desperately need, that we so desperately need to your insight/response.

I look forward to your insight/response.

STOP THE NOISE

STOP THE NOISE

A Physician's Quest to Silence the Politics of Health Care Reform

Brian E. Hill, M.D.

AV Publishing / Marietta GA

STOP THE NOISE
A Physician's Quest to Silence the Politics of
Health Care Reform
All Rights Reserved Copyright © 2010
Brian E. Hill, MD

For Information, please address:
Griffin Publishing Group Imprint
FW Publishing Company, Inc.
P.O. Box 93 / Marietta, GA 30061-0093
Website: www.griffinpublishinggroup.com

Cover Design by Pat Freeman, Graphic Designer

Library of Congress Control Number: 2010938316

ISBN: 978-0-9827994-1-3

Printed in the United States of America

"Well done is better than well said."
Benjamin Franklin

Contents

The Cost of Health Care 1

    Can Government Do It Better? 9

    Medicare versus the Private Sector: A Cost Comparison 11

    Administrative Costs 15

    Profit 27

The Structural Issue: Moral Hazard and Improper Incentives 33

    Moral Hazard and 12 Cents on the Dollar 36

    Cost Sharing 43

    Incentivization 50

    Provider Incentives 59

Massachusetts versus Indiana: From Hypothetical to Reality 67

    The Massachusetts Model 69

    The Indiana Experiment 77

    Massachusetts versus Indiana: Comparative Effectiveness Research 82

The Patient Protection and Affordable Care Act 91

Conclusion 103

Introduction

A multitude of political books line the shelves of bookstores. Some bring great value—they develop a deeper understanding of differing strains of political thought, promote a more thorough evaluation of one's own beliefs, or generate a contrast between alternative styles of governing. However, many books focus on partisan talking points, often relying upon emotion and sensationalism to confound fact and to confirm one particular point of view. They hawk the values, beliefs, and opinions of those who write them. Some are ideological rants, others are a means of accusation, and still others sow discord and dissension. Finger pointing, name calling, derision, demagoguery—this is the approach of so many who comment on the governance of our nation. And little value is gained through such empty rhetoric.

This is not one of those political books. Instead, this is a book based on research, demonstration studies and historical evidence, for I believe that problem solving is best achieved through substantive and honest evaluation of outcome data. I see no value in blind ideology, much less so in those who skew fact and obfuscate truth for personal gain or for the advancement of a political agenda. Viewing the problems impacting our society through the narrowed lens of a dogmatic belief structure will not lead to pragmatic solutions. The citizens of this society lose each time a decision is made and policy is implemented based upon the manipulation of fact to fit into a fixed system of political thought.

Unfortunately, those who are making decisions for this country have seemingly lost the ability to impartially parse the data and reach conclusions that can direct effective legislation. This has not acutely come about with the current administration and is not specific to one political party. This approach has been insidiously building for quite some time, and I do not find it acceptable any longer. The time to alter the practice of politics is upon us; the time for a different approach to curing the problems that we are dealing with as a society is now. We need a new strand of thought to arise. Maybe, at the very least, it is time to reevaluate our current one. And maybe this alteration of political thought can come from a normal citizen, a layperson, from you or me.

I am not sure why I feel in any way able to write something of value, something that others would find meaningful. So much has been written and spoken about with regard to our government, our society, and how those two interact. Who am I to add anything to the volume and depth of discussion? I carry no exaggerated view of self-importance. I am in no way a scholar or an intellectual. I am not on television or radio or in the news media. I am not part of the political class. I do not come from wealth and privilege. I do not carry power or influence.

I am instead a husband, a father and a neighbor. I love my family, my wife and the life we have together. My daughters bring me joy, happiness, some angst, and always love. I would, like most of us with children, do anything to protect them now while safeguarding their future. I am a physician as well. I feel blessed my patients have faith and trust in me to allow me to care for them, to work to restore their lives after illness or disease strikes. And I am the person you see at the grocery store, the community pool, and church. I try to raise my family the best I can, to be a good friend, to be a good neighbor. I try to do what is right, and I hope to make a positive impact in this world, perhaps leaving it a little better than I found it. But the frustration of watching the ineffectiveness of our policy-makers has led me to express my voice, to present my view of this world, to offer a better approach to delineating the problems and developing solutions for the issues impacting our nation.

For we are struggling right now. We are facing daunting issues within our society, and we are in desperate need of effective solutions. We seem to be running from one crisis to another—some we have created, others have been inflicted upon us. We are battling a deep economic recession, persistently high unemployment and home foreclosures. Our news is dominated with charges of racism, cultural clashes, religious conflicts and threats of terror. We are at war, an environmental disaster has developed in the Gulf, Greece is bankrupt, and parts of Europe are struggling to keep their currency afloat amidst mounting debt. America's debt—the debt of each citizen—is staggering and rapidly growing, now reaching $42,709 per person and $119,551 per taxpayer (continuously updated at www.usdebtclock.org). Our public safety nets of Medicare, Medicaid, and Social Security have been manipulated and mismanaged, with decisions based more upon political gamesmanship than economic reality, and they are now unsustainable programs.

These problems are neither new nor unique. War, financial uncertainty, the ebb and flow of an economy, social discord—these inevitably arise in any society. The concern for me and those who I interact with daily is not based upon the presence of these problems. It is the manner with which our elected officials identify and attempt to resolve these issues that is concerning. Why? Because the vision of our country and the future of our society have been snarled amongst the backdrop of politics. We seem to have lost our way. Partisanship and ideology rule, not practicality and pragmatism. There is so much dissention and mistrust, so much hatred and divisiveness. We are being pulled apart, and so many of us feel it. We are unsettled, and we know that all is not right. We can and should do better. We must do better.

This is not a problem with government. Government exists because we allow it to exist, need it to exist. This is not a problem with politics. Politics is the activities involved in managing our government by those we elect to fulfill such duties. This is not a problem with society, because society is the entity that develops out of our system of rules and norms. We as individuals are to blame. We have become comfortable and complacent. We have abdicated our duty to be the caretakers of our government and to maintain a level of accountability from our lawmakers.

We have allowed our elected officials to become the negative connotation associated with their title: politicians. We all say it, hear it and likely believe it: Politics is dirty, politicians are just trying to do what they can to get elected, oh, that's just politics. But is it really okay for our elected officials to mislead the public, to steal, to not pay taxes, to lie, to serve themselves all while maintaining the façade of caring for our country, of caring for you and me? Should those who lead our country be allowed to wallow in the mire of this depravity? Because if we continue to allow this type of politics to be the norm, to be acceptable, can a civil and honest society really develop out of the policies put forth by such people?

I do worry about today. While the nature of the issues we face are timeless, having existed from civilization to civilization, our window to identify and correct them is not. We have done little other than continue to dig a deeper hole for ourselves, and time is running short. Unless we begin to properly resolve the issues we face, the harm of inactivity and flawed legislation will irrevocably damage the strength of our nation. And for that reason, I worry most about the future of our country. That is my children's future, our children's future, and they deserve better. They will be the ones who have to deal with this mountain of debt and litany of unresolved problems, the result of our selfishness and incompetence. We truly are placing a tremendous burden upon them. Their standard of living will be less than ours. They will be taxed more and receive less; they will have less opportunity and higher unemployment. They will have to work harder to pay off our shortcomings, our shortsightedness, our inability to properly solve problems.

We cannot continue down this path; we cannot allow our generation to handcuff the future of our society. Change will only come about when we as citizens demand it. But to demand change requires involvement, attentiveness, and knowledge. Complacency, the other option, will beget failure. The goal of this book is to pass along a little of the knowledge that I have gained in my reading to hopefully add clarity for others.

Specifically, I am going breakdown the health care reform process as an example of the failure of the current political approach (practiced by both major parties). Before I get to the policy endpoint that arose from the debate, the legislation called the Patient Protection and Affordable Care Act (PPACA) that became law on March 23, 2010, I am going to discuss data, studies, and historical models in an attempt to add more transparency and knowledge, to more openly delineate the arguments and hopefully add to the discussion. I want to stop the noise of politics that subterfuges honest evaluation of the outcome of policy; noise that diminishes the likelihood for developing plans to solve the issues that we as a nation face.

Prior to taking that step, I'll give a little background about my involvement. About a year ago, I was like most when it came to politics: not uninformed but certainly not involved. I would read the newspapers and several online news sites daily, would occasionally speak to colleagues about current political topics, and would complain to my friends or family about policies that did not seem to mesh with reality. But I was comfortable. I loved being a physician. I had a quiet and fulfilling personal life. And I really was not too concerned that the policymakers would impact the goals that I had established for my life and my children's lives. Then the health care debate began. I wholeheartedly agreed that it was well beyond time to address the inadequacies of the health care delivery system in the U.S., and I was happy to see that our President was able to advance the topic beyond preliminary discussions. So I began like most to follow the debate from the periphery. As the rhetoric rose and the ideas being put forth gelled and moved toward potential policy, I developed greater interest. And I began to read more when it appeared that the U.S. House of Representatives was moving toward a public option plan. I wanted to better understand how these policy ideas would impact my practice, my patients and my nation.

Fortunately, my Congressman was coming home for summer recess, so I called his office to see if he would be holding a town hall meeting to discuss his thoughts with us, his constituents, on the health care reform process. To my chagrin, his staff informed me that he would not be holding any events focusing on health care. But I was told that he had scheduled a meeting near my home to discuss a local road project. After deciding to attend late Friday evening, I called my father-in-law early Saturday morning and asked if he would be interested in joining me for the meeting. I had collected data on the public option and was concerned that the information I had come across did not jive with the rosy predictions our Representatives were presenting to the public. I wanted to ask my Congressman a question.

I waited four hours in the meeting, allowing those attending the meeting about the road project to have their concerns addressed. I did not speak out. I did not interrupt. Finally, the microphone was opened for other issues, and I stepped up and asked my Congressman a question regarding data on the public option plan. I was not belligerent. I was not accusatory. I was not inflammatory. I relayed information. I was a doctor worried that the health care changes being espoused by my Congressman, someone who has no idea about the practice of medicine, would negatively impact our health care system and the quality of care that my patients would be able to receive. I wanted to have some assurance that he had thoroughly evaluated his stance on such an important topic and was not just following the direction of his political party. This was too important of an issue to be uninformed and complacent, for the outcome of the reform of our health care system would lead to lasting effects resonating through future generations.

However, instead of responding intelligently and thoughtfully, my Congressman began to rant and berate and insult. Not only did he not know the answer to my question, but he could not put forth a coherent explanation for his belief. Instead, he struck out at me as though I should not in any way challenge him. He accused me of hijacking the meeting and insinuated that I was not from his district. For a bit of irony, I do live in the district and he does not. The meeting ended, my question remained unanswered, and nothing was resolved. Political ideology and emotion, not fact and honest evaluation, had trumped the discussion.

But the health care debate was just beginning to grow. As if the interaction with my Congressman was not sufficient enough to ignite a fire in me, a few days later on August 12, 2009, President Obama, at a town hall in Portsmouth, NH stated, *"...if a family care physician works with his patient (a diabetic)....they might get reimbursed a pittance, but if they get their foot amputated, that's 30, 40, 50 thousand dollars the surgeon gets reimbursed immediately."* The President blatantly insinuated that doctors cut off legs of diabetics out of their own laziness and greed. Not only was this statement incredibly offensive and an affront to the ethics of those of us in the medical community, but the President's reimbursement numbers were completely inaccurate and misleading (the average reimbursement for a below-knee amputation and the following 90 days of care is $700 to $1,000). This further motivated me, and I began to read more and study more, and the more I did, the greater my concern grew.

This concern was not and is not born out of political ideology. I quickly realized that this had nothing to do with either my Congressman or the President; this was about the practice of medicine and the ability of my patients to receive quality care. I see no role for political ideology in treating illness and disease. Political ideology is noise and distraction that clouds sound judgment. Illness and disease do not prejudiciously inflict their pain and suffering based on political affiliation. I do not see a Democrat prostate cancer, a Libertarian kidney cancer, or a Republican bladder cancer. I treat people, and I choose treatment based upon evidence and data that direct me to the best chance of cure.

I have taken the same approach to evaluating the health care reform ideas. Physicians practice what we call evidence-based medicine, meaning that we utilize outcome data obtained from research studies and trials and history in order to determine the best approach to treat disease. If the outcome data from a treatment does not demonstrate efficacy, then that idea is cast aside and a different treatment path is chosen. For example, let's say I arrange a research trial for a possible new treatment for prostate cancer. Perhaps I believe that eating pine bark will cure the cancer. So I have my patients eat pine bark for a year and I then evaluate the response of the cancer to this modality. If I find that the cancer has progressed, then I do not continue my patients on pine bark as therapy for prostate cancer. The outcome evidence demonstrates a lack of efficacy. And if I were to develop another trial, I would not place pine bark at the center of that trial. In doing so, I am ignoring the evidence. As the oft-mentioned quote from Einstein states, "The definition of insanity is doing the same thing over and over again and expecting a different result."

Yet the more I looked at the health care reform, the more I saw a lack of utilization of this simple principle. On the contrary, it seemed as though the reform process was the antithesis of this model. Instead of applying the same evidence-based approach to cure the ills and correct the underlying fundamental flaws within the health care delivery system, I saw politics wreaking havoc. There were half-truths, outright lies, self-serving announcements and pronouncements, greed and corruption and shadiness. There was deal-making; excuses; finger-pointing; demonization of industries, people and groups; there were winners and losers, special favors, and outright bribery. All once again done in the name of politics, none for the sake of my patients. And that was a shame because we had a tremendous opportunity to truly transform our health care system, to bring about that which we all desire: to increase access to a highly-efficient, high-quality health care system in a cost-effective manner.

Actually, it is more than a shame. We should be incensed. This is our health and the health of our children and their children. Those who are suddenly struck with an acute illness or a cancer diagnosis or have to deal with chronic disease will tell you how precious and fleeting health can be. Health is not appreciated until it is taken away. As I heard someone mention during the health care debates that summer, "You can go broke over and over, but you only die once."

In addition to utilizing the evidence-based approach that is the staple of current medical practice, shouldn't the reform process also encompass the overriding rule of medicine, the Hippocratic Oath? "I will follow that system of regimen which, according to my ability and judgment, I consider for the benefit of my patients, and abstain from whatever is deleterious and mischievous." When I treat a patient, my first principle of care is to add quality and value to that person's life, choosing those treatments that above all do no harm. The choice of health care reform must be implemented following the same principle. We have to be certain that our reform choices meet the highest of standards where the cost of medicine is decreased, access is increased, and quality is maintained (and hopefully improved). These three goals are the pillars upon which the transformation of health care should be based.

When political wrangling and arbitrary decision-making dominate the discussion, medicine suffers and people suffer. We cannot afford to choose unproven plans that arise out of political gain and carry potential for failure, much less plans that have demonstrated failure (more about this later). Our health is just too valuable. So let's methodically but expeditiously move toward evidence-driven solutions that do no harm. Let's honestly evaluate outcome data to ensure we are achieving our goals in reforming our health care system. Stubbornly holding on to ideology in the face of outcome evidence that points to failed policy harms us all. In the end, even the politician and the ideologue lose.

This is the disclaimer section, and I only do this to be as open and honest as possible. I am a physician. I am not a health policy expert. I spend my days taking care of people, a portion of my nights loving my family and the remainder of my time reading. I have written this without a staff (save my wife), without a research team, and without a statistician or economist. The breadth of information is endless, and I am well aware that I have only touched on a small portion of that which has been written. I in no way expect this to be an exhaustive look at the entirety of research. There is more to the economics of health care than I can identify; more that I even know to search out. But I have also become aware that the problems that exist beyond the scope of my reading are secondary to the structural issues plaguing our system, and those more intricate problems can be addressed once the global issues are resolved. I am not going to touch on every aspect of health care. I will leave the discussion regarding interstate commerce, tort reform, fraud, state high risk pools, and the impact of insurance reform for another day. While these are critical to maximizing the overall efficiency of the system, they only work at the edges and do not impact the true structural problem.

I am going to mostly focus on the cost of health care. Not because I do not see the need to extend access or enhance quality, but if we do not fix the cost problem, then access and quality can never be improved. While these are not mutually exclusive concepts, and alterations in one impact the other, the cost issue is at the center of our problem. Simply stated, if our reform process does not correct an unsustainable cost problem, then how can we afford broader coverage or better care? This is the practicality of the economics of this world. (I do believe though that decreasing the cost of health care will lead to greater access.)

To relate this to medicine, let's look at the ABC's of trauma—Airway, Breathing and Circulation. The idea is based on stratification of need. If a patient presents in respiratory arrest following a motor vehicle accident, you do not first tend to an open leg fracture. Doing so may make the patient look better, but nothing is being done to increase the likelihood of the patient seeing tomorrow. The obstructed airway is the most pressing need that must be corrected before further problems are addressed. We can at times cover multiple issues at once, but the focus always needs to remain steadfast on that which is most directly related to survival. Cost is my Airway.

I will first cover the cost impact on our society to give an overview of the problem. I will then discuss the components of the cost problem more specifically. Cost in medicine comes from multiple sources but can be grouped into a two broad categories: the cost of managing the system and the cost of utilizing the system. The management or administrative costs of either the government or the private industry arise from collecting and distributing (based on contracts) the pooled funds of the health insurer's beneficiaries (the insured). Providers of medical care are impacted by these costs as well, for they need to interact with the insurer in the exchange of the fee for the service provided. I discuss administrative costs in order to determine whether the government or the private sector is able to deliver health care in a more cost-effective manner. If one is more efficient, then we need to focus our solutions around that entity.

Once we have answered the question about who best manages the system, we can then delve into determining how to create the most efficient system. The focus moves to the evaluation of the issues that are impacting the ability of our system to provide cost-effective care and approaches solutions for these issues in an evidence-based manner.

This is where utilization comes into play. Cost comes from patients accessing the health care system. This is related to volume, but increases in cost also arise from the use of new technology and new drugs. Medical advancements undoubtedly increase cost, but correcting the cost problem should not negatively impact the ability of medicine to improve its product. It is the appropriate application of technology that must be fostered. And its application needs to occur in a health care system that promotes proper utilization by the two direct participants in the system: the patient and the provider. This is where, after spending so much time reading and looking at different studies and health care systems and approaches to the reform process that I find the true crux of the matter. For that reason, I will spend time focusing on moral hazard and misaligned incentives. It is the confluence of these two issues within our health care system's current structure that creates a milieu where overutilization is incented for the provider without restraint from the patient. The data that led me to this conclusion is covered in detail.

Finally, I move the discussion from the realm of studies and data to the real-world application of the differing approaches to reform. The outcome data drawn from actively functioning societal models should carry tremendous sway. I tell my patients after a surgery or a medication change that the proof is in the pudding: The studies direct us toward the best option for cure, but it is the outcome that matters. The patient, just like these real-world models, lets us know the level of success of our intervention. So let's silence the noise that distracts from true solutions and pursue the outcome data that direct us down the best path to heal this broken system. And in evaluating the health care reform process in this manner, we may see a potential alternative to the current political practice that will truly enhance the ability of our government to identify and solve the problems impacting our nation.

THE COST OF HEALTH CARE

The current trajectory of health care spending in the U.S. is unsustainable and bankrupting our nation, and this mantra was put forth throughout the reform debate. The goal of bending the cost curve downward initially dominated the discussion and for good reason. The following information regarding costs are based upon projections that do not take into account the Patient Protection and Affordable Care Act (PPACA) signed into law in March 2010. The impact of that legislation upon projected health care expenditures will be discussed later. I will not dwell too long on that which most agree upon—our health care system is too costly—but the information is presented to deliver a full understanding of the extent of this issue.

According to the U.S. Department of Health and Human Services (HHS), our national health expenditures, which are every single dollar spent on health care in the U.S., approached $2.5 trillion in 2009.[1] This was an increase of 5.7 percent from 2008 ($2.3 trillion) and occurred at a time when the economy shrank 1.1 percent. National health care expenditures in 2009 accounted for 17.3 percent of our gross domestic product (total revenue generated from every source within the U.S., $14.1 trillion in 2009), up from 16.2 percent in 2008 and 13.2 percent in 2000.

Unfortunately, the expenditures are continuing to rise. This is the upward bending cost curve that needs to be corrected. HHS has projected that "over the period (2009-2019), average annual health spending growth (6.1 percent) is anticipated to outpace average annual growth in the overall economy (4.4 percent)."[1] If we continue on this projected path, national health care expenditures are expected to reach a whopping $4.7 trillion by 2019. This is calculated to consume 20.6 percent of our nation's gross domestic product, equating to approximately $14,000 per person and $56,000 for a family of four.[2] Without reform, one out of every five dollars spent in the U.S. in 2019 will go to health care.

This is similar to the adjustable rate mortgages that are driving people out of their homes. The interest rates on the mortgages can adjust upward every year. If the interest rate increases more than the rate of salary growth for the homeowner, then the cost of the mortgage begins to eat up more and more of the monthly take-home pay, requiring the homeowner to dip into savings. If this situation persists, then the choice eventually gets narrowed to paying the mortgage or purchasing other necessities of life. It is a poor choice that potentially leads to a bad outcome—bankruptcy and/or foreclosure.

Public sector (government) spending is growing more rapidly than the private sector. From 2009 through 2019, Medicare and Medicaid spending growth are projected to average 6.9 percent and 7.9 percent annually, greatly exceeding the incremental cost increase in the private sector.[1] And remember, this is despite the fact that our economy is growing at a much slower rate of 4.4 percent.

This is particularly worrisome when taking into account the current financial situation of the Medicare Trust Fund, a fund established by Congress that accounts for all program income and disbursements to cover medical care for the population over the age of 65. Without getting too deep into the intricacies of Medicare, the Trust Fund is broken into two main components. The first is the Hospital Insurance (HI) Trust Fund, also known as Medicare Part A. It is mostly financed through payroll taxes and covers inpatient hospital stays, skilled nursing facilities and hospice care. The second is the Supplemental Medical Insurance Trust Fund, and this includes Medicare Parts B, C, and D. This covers a portion of expenses associated with physician office visits, outpatient surgery, laboratory testing, medications and other medical services. This is supported through enrollee premiums (the cost of the insurance plan) and congressional authorization of funds, meaning money collected via general taxation.

The Trustees managing the Trust Fund reported in 2009 that Medicare is facing significant financial difficulties. Outlays to pay for medical care exceeded income from taxation and premium collection in 2008, requiring the Fund to dip into its reserves (its savings account). The shortfall amount between outlays and revenue is expected to rapidly increase in all future years. This is the definition of an unsustainable path. The projected date of HI Trust Fund exhaustion is 2017. The following is taken from the summary of the 2009 Annual Report:

"The projected exhaustion of the HI Trust Fund within the next eight years is an urgent concern. Congressional action will be necessary to ensure uninterrupted provision of HI services to beneficiaries. Correcting the financial imbalance for the HI Trust Fund—even in the short range alone—will require substantial changes to program income and/or expenditures...Its cost growth can be contained without sacrificing quality of care only if health care cost growth more generally is contained. But despite the difficulties—indeed, because of the difficulties—it is essential that action be taken soon, particularly to control health care costs..."[3]

In order to minimize this discrepancy in the short term, HHS expects "about one quarter of Part B enrollees will be subject to unusually large premium increases in the next two years." But even after increasing the shared expense for Medicare beneficiaries, the future is still bleak unless further balance is restored between revenue and expenditures. And this problem worsens with each passing day.

As the population ages over the next 20 years, the number of people on Medicare is expected to rise from 46 million to 79 million. During this time, the ratio of workers paying to sustain this system for each patient receiving benefits is projected to decline from 3.7 to 2.4.[4] This inverse relationship portends a dire outcome. To add further clarity and weight to this point, it is important to review the financing behind Medicare. As mentioned, Medicare is partially financed through payroll taxes, so workers pay into the system throughout their careers. Initially, since the U.S had a younger population and life expectancy was shorter, a surplus developed and was placed in the Medicare Trust Fund to be used to pay for the health care expenses as that generation of workers retired.

However, we are living longer, we have aged as a society and health care costs have risen. Medicare is currently paying out more per beneficiary than what the beneficiary had paid into the system while working.

The cost to sustain the growing Medicare population is now being shifted to a shrinking working population. A 50 percent reduction in the workforce is paying into the system to support a 72 percent increase in beneficiaries. This will do nothing but accelerate the decline of an already unsustainable model. To convey the extent of the expected financial shortfall of this program, the 2009 Trustees report regarding the unfunded liability—the amount of money needed to fulfill the health care obligations for future generations as they hit the age of 65—was estimated at $38 trillion over the next 75 years. Medicare cannot continue down this path. It is just not a fiscally viable program as it is currently structured.

The cost issue is not unique to Medicare, however. The burden extends beyond the public realm and impacts every segment of society. According to the Bureau of Labor and Statistics, employer costs for employee health care coverage have increased steadily since 1960 as a percentage of hourly wages and salaries, accounting for 8.2 percent of total compensation in 2009.[5] This equates to $2.40 for every hour worked, a dollar figure that decreases the usable wages of employees.

Furthermore, the cost escalation has impacted the ability of businesses to cover insurance. While large corporations provide health insurance coverage to more than 98 percent of their employees, only 59 percent of firms with less than 200 employees offer such benefits, a decrease of 10 percent over the last 10 years.[6] In the Kaiser Family Foundation (KFF) annual reporting of Employer Health Benefits for 2009, firms were questioned about expected benefit changes for year 2010. KFF found that "among those that offer benefits, large percentages of firms report that in the next year they are very or somewhat likely to increase the amount workers contribute to premiums (42%), increase deductible amounts (36%), increase office visit cost sharing (39%), or increase the amount that employees have to pay for prescription drugs (37%)."[6]

The competitiveness of U.S. businesses in the global economy has also been mentioned as being negatively impacted by the increasing costs of providing employer-based health insurance. Since businesses more often than not are the supplier of health insurance coverage, it would make the argument seem quite simple. A Health Policy Brief by the New American Foundation in May 2009 stated that the employer health care burden puts U.S. firms at a competitive disadvantage against foreign firms. It noted, for example, that employer-sponsored health insurance adds $1,500 to the production cost of an automobile. It also mentioned that U.S. manufacturing firms pay twice as much per hourly wage for health benefits as compared to our trading partners.[7]

While I agree that the added costs of escalating health insurance premiums do not benefit American enterprise, I do want to pause briefly and dissect this supposition that our contemporaries gain an advantage. This is where we need to be careful and not bring noise into the discussion.

Health insurance, no matter how the system is arranged, is not free. While most of the health care insurance costs in the U.S. are paid directly by employers, a majority of such costs in the countries of our trading partners with socialized medicine are paid through general taxation. And these taxes to pay for health care raise the cost of goods, albeit in a more indirect fashion, while also creating economic distortions, points often left out of such arguments.

For example, the Value Added Tax (VAT) in the United Kingdom (U.K.), a tax on the estimated market value added to a product as it moves through each stage of production, currently resides at 17.5 percent and is set to rise to 20 percent in January 2011. This is the third largest form of tax collection in the U.K. While this tax falls under a provision in the General Agreement on Tariffs and Trade (GATT) that allows the exclusion of indirect taxes like the VAT from exports and allows it to be applied to imports, the tax, as all taxes do, impacts economic behavior. A study by Martin Feldstein and Paul Krugman evaluating the impact of the VAT on international trade found that its introduction most likely leads to a decline in exports based upon its allocation to tradable goods as opposed to non-tradable goods and services.[8] Diminishing exports negatively impacts economic expansion and demonstrates the effect of these taxes on those corporations that are competing in the world market. The VAT is one portion of the tax burden used to support the health care system in the U.K., and the point above is just one instance of the economic distortion of taxation that undermines productivity.

I make note of this to demonstrate that arguments in papers are not always credible, and the conclusions drawn by studies or briefs such as the one from the New American Foundation may not be as straightforward as they seem. To propose that our health care system creates a greater drag than our competing nations without properly accounting for all variables brings little value to the discussion. That said, the rising health care costs borne by U.S. businesses do decrease jobs, impact workers' salaries, increase the costs of goods and create an unnecessary drag on our economy. We could undoubtedly gain further advantage in the global economy through the transformation of our health care system into one that is more efficient.

The cost of health care affects us directly as individuals as well. According to an article in The American Journal of Medicine, health care expenses accounted for 62 percent of U.S. personal bankruptcies in 2007.[9] Even those who do not face bankruptcy from these rising costs still maintain a level of concern with regard to their finances and the impact of an illness upon financial well-being.

I am going to digress for a moment and present a few different perspectives on health care and our society. We have a tendency to get wrapped up in the cost issue and miss other salient points. The idea behind this discussion is to raise these other views that hopefully add value to the topic—this is in no way an attempt to downplay the significant financial burden that our society faces.

The first observation is to examine the cost to receive annual prostate cancer screening in my office for a new patient. Medical collusion law makes it is illegal for me to post what I get paid by private insurance, so I will use the 2009 Medicare fee schedule to pass along the charges associated with that visit. A physical exam and a prostate specific antigen (PSA) blood test will run $91.97 (level 3 moderately complex office visit) and $26 (payment on an average charge of $79), respectively. After adding $6 for the blood draw and specimen handling, the total cost is $124. Obviously a visit for a more thorough evaluation that includes diabetes screening, cholesterol levels, kidney and liver function, cervical cancer screening with a pap smear or breast cancer screening with a mammogram would incur greater cost, but the example above at least delivers a general idea. And of course, it relays nothing about the cost if an abnormality is found.

But where does this cost fall among other "necessary" aspects of American life? The average digital TV costs $690; a pack-a-day smoker at $4 per pack will spend over $1,460 a year; the average cell phone bill is $635.85 per year; the average annual cable bill is $852. How about a $2 cup of coffee on the way to work every day? Our comparative examples can go on and on, but I think the point is obvious. I have taken care of the occasional patient who complains about the cost of medical care while carrying the newest cell phone on a hip holster and a pack of cigarettes in the front pocket. Perhaps a portion of the ongoing cost issue is representative of misplaced priorities. Maybe societal priorities and the appropriate level of personal responsibility for our individual health care costs need to be reevaluated as well.

To move on to another tangent—when looking at our society in the context of history, I feel compelled to point out that increases in health care spending are not necessarily bad. Perhaps America spends more money on health care because it has advanced as a nation and our society now has the additional resources to do so. We do not have to individually grow food, our houses have indoor plumbing, we drive automobiles for rapid transit, we have advanced telecommunications, we mass produce essential items at lower cost...and we have expanded medicine beyond penicillin to treat infection and death as the expected outcome of cancer. This is health care viewed through Maslow's Hierarchy of Needs. Our society has moved past the basic survival and safety needs and can focus a greater amount of resources on items beyond simply avoiding death. We can now train our sights on curing illness and living longer, healthier lives.

Along a similar train of thought, I do not mind seeing reports of U.S. health care expenditures compared to other industrialized nations where the U.S. is reported to spend so much more than our counterparts. That falls under extraneous information if presented without context. Because ultimately, when we compare our societal expenses with others, the real issue is not one of cost—it is one of value.

Our model must uphold the ideal of prevention of disease and a healthy lifestyle, not only disease management. We must construct a system that promotes the development of new diagnostic tools to better detect disease. We must be able to continue to search for novel medications and alternative treatments that aid in the advancement of medicine and increase our chances to cure. When disease strikes, our system must allow for the application of technological innovations that provide less pain and suffering. And if this happens at a greater cost than the other industrialized nations, then that should be acceptable, for we are receiving value for our health care dollars. But if this is not the case, if we are not obtaining improved outcomes despite greater cost, if we are not advancing medicine beyond the confines of our current knowledge and abilities, then we must properly delineate and correct the inadequacies of our system that inhibit efficient functioning and the realization of maximal value.

I believe that we as Americans have a unique view of life, one that is very different than our counterparts from other nations. We as a society value life and strive to squeeze every day, month and year, every ounce of living out of our existence. It is important to us. We are more individualistic, more self-driven than society-driven. It is part of the American spirit that has served our country so well, that rugged individualism and self-determination. And it extends into medicine and our expectation of the practice of medicine.

But that expectation will cost. It is why we spend money on third line chemotherapy agents that are exorbitantly expensive and are often unavailable in other countries; it is why we pursue knee replacements to maximize the quality of our time on this earth; it is why we perform robotic surgery to minimize pain. It is why, when we hold a premature 24-week old baby in the palm of our hand, we count that child as a living being, and we do everything within our power to save that life (and please don't quote to me the numbers on higher U.S. infant mortality rates without making sure the data is based on an apples-to-apples comparison first: that falls under noise). Again, these things cost, but perhaps we as a society dictate that this is our view, our priority, our culture, and this approach to medical care fits our goals and desires for this brief existence.

If this is true, then we need to uncover ways to not minimize the offering of these medical advancements but instead find ways to more efficiently bring them to the market, to more efficiently utilize health care dollars so that we are able to continue to deliver that which we find valuable to the entirety of our society. We want medical technology to continue to progress; we want to continue to strive to find the one medicine, the one treatment, the one cure that relieves human suffering. But in order to do so, we need to make sure that the structure of our health care system does not lead to unnecessary expenditures, to redundancy and waste, to improper incentivizes for providers and patients.

We are all well aware of these cost issues, and while we may disagree on some of the numbers being tossed about, none would argue that we can and should do better. No one wants to see inefficiency inhibit our ability to progress. So how can we gain more value for our expenditures? Is this better achieved through more government involvement, or can the private sector do better? Are there models that we can evaluate? Is there information available to help direct us down a better pathway? Or do we just put some "health care experts" together, come up with a plan and hope for the best?

Can Government Do It Better?

To be a bit light but to again bring that common sense theme to the forefront: how many remember joking about the news reports of our federal government paying tens of thousands of dollars for mundane items such as toilets and screws and wrenches? I am not going to run down the list of excessiveness associated with government spending, for I believe that it is a broadly accepted and well-documented phenomenon. If that is the case, do many (any) believe that government is truly an efficient steward of our money, with the emphasis on efficient?

Each of us needs to pause for a moment and answer this honestly. For while this seems to be a simple and perhaps rhetorical question, if we are planning on expanding the role of government further into health care, an industry that currently costs $2.5 trillion, do we not think that this matter actually requires more than a passing remark, a joke, or worse yet a general level of acceptance? We are expected for some reason to faithfully believe that the government, whether under control of either Republicans or Democrats, will change its patterns of inefficient spending despite decades of evidence to the contrary.

When looking for a babysitter, do you first ensure that the person watching your children does not have a past pattern of child abuse? And if that person did, would you hire them anyway? And if you had to choose someone to manage your family's budget, would you not look to see how they performed managing other people's money or their own finances before handing your life savings to them? Wouldn't that be prudent? Yet we often ignore such careful consideration when deciding the best manager of the health care system, a system that impacts every aspect of our lives and plays such an intricate role in our human experience. I err toward prudence, so I look at past and current performance as a guide.

To generate this historical perspective for government management, I could write about Amtrak, the government established, subsidized and persistently bankrupted railway that has yet to make a profit over the past 40 years and cost the taxpayers $1.3 billion to keep afloat in 2008 alone. It cost $285 million just to service the debt in 2008.[10] I could go on about the U.S. Postal Service with its $8 billion deficit over the last year and projected retirement liability of $238 billion by 2020. I could discuss our government-run educational system where we rank third in industrialized nations in educational spending as percent of our gross domestic product yet continue to fall behind in test scores. Each of these can be debated for their value to society and the willingness of our citizenry to accept a loss to maintain a service. But those discussions are for another time. This is about government efficiency.

Perhaps the most telling insight into the lack of efficiency in the government comes from Peter Orszag who previously directed the Congressional Budget Office and stepped down in July 2010 as President Obama's director of Office of Management and Budget. Immediately following his resignation, he was quoted in The Daily Beast. "Two-thirds of Americans believe that when something is run by government it is inefficient and wasteful," he said, citing a study from the Pew Center. "And they are right… In too many examples, the government spends money not out of need but out of inertia."[11]

Please do not get me wrong. I am not here to beat the drum of the evils of government. Government is a necessary part of our society. I just want to bring sensibility to the discussion, a framework of common sense and honest evaluation of the ability of our government to work in an efficient and effective manner, particularly as it relates to its capacity to deliver goods and services to society. Again, I want to be prudent, and history can be a great teacher if we listen to its lessons.

Medicare versus the Private Sector: A Cost Comparison

In order to begin to uncover the underlying cost discrepancies in health care management between the private sector and the government, we need to evaluate their individual abilities to control cost at a more general level. The following section attempts to bring a direct comparison in cost containment between these two entities, hopefully controlling those confounding variables that lead down the path to erroneous conclusions.

Medicare was established in 1965 as a $3 billion government-managed insurance program for those ages 65 and over. Soon after its implementation, the House Ways and Means Committee conservatively estimated that by 1990 it would cost about $12 billion, a figure that was adjusted for inflation at that time. The true cost of Medicare in 1990 was actually $107 billion. The estimate was off by a factor of 9 (they undershot by 900%). Medicare has since continued its rapid upward cost trajectory, with expenditures reaching $470 billion in 2009. While we see that the original cost estimate was far from precise, and while the costs continue to rise, the question that really needs to be addressed is: How does this rise in cost compare to the private sector? For while health care costs as a whole are increasing, determining which sector has historically demonstrated a greater ability to control this rise conveys valuable information.

Since 1970 Medicare and Medicaid costs per patient have risen 33 percent more than the combined costs of all other health care in America, i.e. the private sector.[12,13] An important point to note to minimize confusion is that this discussion is based on the rate of rise—the increase in expenditures over time—not overall health care costs. The argument supporting this as an expected phenomenon seems fairly obvious: the elderly are more ill and their costs would be expected to rise more quickly than the younger, healthier population. Technological and medical advancements, part of the drivers of increasing medical costs, would be utilized more often in this subset of the population and their personal health care costs should consequently rise more quickly as well.

While this thought process would intuitively seem true, the data contradicts this supposition. From 1987 to 2004, the Centers for Medicare and Medicaid Services (CMS) evaluated total personal health care spending per capita, defined as the amount of money spent to treat an individual, and broke the data down by age group.[14] Surprisingly, the greatest increase in personal health care spending was found in the 0-18 year old age range where the average annual growth rate was 6.8 percent. In the age range from 19-64 years, the growth rate was 6.6 percent. In the Medicare population (65 and older), the rate of growth was 6.2 percent. This breakdown flies contrary to the preconceived notion and begs the question: Why is the cost to manage the health of an individual rising more quickly with Medicare compared to the private sector when personal health care costs are rising more quickly in the latter group? This would be the same as a car driving for less distance on a tank of gas despite getting more miles per gallon. And this trend of increased cost per beneficiary for Medicare has been demonstrated in other evaluations of the data.

According to another study outlined in Figure 1, the cost per beneficiary for Medicare increased 37.8 percent more than the private sector from 1997 to 2005 (10.6 percent versus 7.7 percent, respectively).[15] And again, the previous CMS data demonstrates that this is not occurring in the elderly population as a result of increased medical costs directly associated with receiving health care. Another factor other than direct patient health care costs must account for this disparity.

Jacob Hacker Ph.D., a political science professor at Yale who is often credited as the "father of the public option", has authored a study that runs contrary to these findings. He wrote:

"By way of illustration, between 1997 and 2006, health spending per enrollee (for comparable benefits) grew at 4.6 percent a year under Medicare, compared with 7.3 percent a year under private health insurance."[16]

While Hacker's data on the growth of health care costs in the private insurance group closely matched the research by the Heritage Foundation seen in Figure 1—7.7 percent versus Hacker's 7.3 percent—his findings for Medicare were quite different—Heritage 10.6 percent versus Hacker's 4.6 percent. Hacker argues that for comparable benefits Medicare has performed better at cost control, with private health insurance spending rising 59 percent more quickly than Medicare (7.3 percent divided by 4.6 percent). So who are we to believe? How can two studies come to disparate conclusions? As is usually the case, the devil is in the details.

Per-Beneficiary Spending Growth, 1997–2005, by Source of Funds

	Spending on Medicare Beneficiaries, by Source (Dollars per Medicare Beneficiary and Percent of Total)					Spending on Privately Insured and Uninsured, by Source, Excluding All Spending on Medicare Beneficiaries (Dollars per Person and Percent of Total)			
	Medicare Spending	Out of Pocket	Private Insurance	Medicaid and Other Public	Total per Medicare Beneficiary	Private Insurance	Out of Pocket	Other Private Sources	Total Per Non-Medicare Beneficiary
1997									
Dollars	$3,925	$625	$662	$227	$5,438	$1,977	$585	$567	$3,128
% of Total	72.2%	11.5%	12.2%	4.2%	100.0%	63.2%	18.7%	18.1%	100.0%
2005									
Dollars	$6,180	$1,910	$2,603	$1,463	$12,157	$3,667	$1,165	$851	$5,682
% of Total	50.8%	15.7%	21.4%	12.0%	100.0%	64.5%	20.5%	15.0%	100.0%
Growth, 1997–2005									
Cumulative	57.5%	205.6%	293.5%	545.7%	123.6%	85.5%	99.2%	50.1%	81.7%
Average Annual	5.8%	15.0%	18.7%	26.3%	10.6%	8.0%	9.0%	5.2%	7.7%

Sources: 1997 spending data on Medicare beneficiaries: Centers for Medicare and Medicaid Services, *Health and Health Care of the Medicare Population*, 1997, pp. 98–117, Tables 4.2–4 6, at http://www.cms.hhs.gov/MCBS/Downloads/HHC_1997_section4.pdf (July 2, 2009). 2005 spending data on Medicare beneficiaries: Medicare Payment Advisory Commission, *A Data Book: Healthcare Spending and the Medicare Program*, June 2008, p. 63, at http://medpac.gov/documents/jun08DataBook_Entire_report.pdf (July 2, 2009). Spending data for private insurance: author's calculations based on Medicare figures shown and Centers for Medicare and Medicaid Services, National Health Expenditures Web Tables, pp. 15–16, Table 13, at http://www.cms.hhs.gov/NationalHealthExpendData/downloads/tables.pdf (July 2, 2009). Growth rates: author's calculations based on other figures shown.

Table 2 • B 2301 ☎ heritage.org

Figure 1. Per-beneficiary Spending Growth, Medicare versus Privately Insured/Uninsured. Used by permission.

First a side point that does not impact the calculations: A congressional study concluded that Medicare is the least generous of the leading forms of health insurance and is not comparable to private insurance. The Medicare Payment Advisory Commission reinforced this finding when they found that as of 2005 only 11 percent of Medicare beneficiaries relied exclusively on Medicare for their health coverage.[17,18] Medicare beneficiaries purchase secondary insurance at such a high rate because Medicare does not sufficiently cover the broad range of medical costs as seen in the private sector where secondary insurance is rare. So to portray

Medicare benefits as comparable with those in the private sector brings more noise, not truth, into the debate. It is important to ensure that the conveyed information delivers true direct comparisons; otherwise the best solutions will be missed.

More important and directly related to the cost issue, Medicare has covered less and less of the total health care costs per beneficiary over time, instead shifting a greater burden onto seniors. Out-of-pocket spending increased from 11.5 percent to 15.7 percent from 1997 to 2005. Over that same period, a growing share of Medicare beneficiaries' health costs were shifted to private or supplemental insurance, with that share of spending rising from 12.2 percent to 21.4 percent. Taken together, Medicare's share of its beneficiaries' costs has dropped from 72.2 percent to 50.8 percent. By comparison, the share of health care costs paid by private insurance for its beneficiaries over this timeframe has increased slightly from 63.2 percent to 64.5 percent.[15] This is in no way a commentary on the pros and cons of cost sharing (costs that a beneficiary inputs for care, a discussion that will come later) but rather an attempt to create a more direct comparison. If the beneficiary's growing burden of cost sharing is excluded, Medicare spending appears to grow more slowly than the private sector. However, when these costs are appropriately accounted for, we see that total health care spending is growing more rapidly per Medicare beneficiary. It is misleading to characterize costs in any other way.

But this is what Hacker did with his calculations. He looked at the expenditures from Medicare's perspective alone, not the total health care expenditures for the Medicare patient. Basically, he only incorporated a portion of the total cost to manage a less generous program. As an example, consider a college student with an annual educational cost of $10,000. If she gets a scholarship for $2,000, then her personal cost decreases to $8,000. But the total cost of her education has not decreased. It still costs $10,000 a year; the cost is now being shared. It would be erroneous to only count the student's cost and conclude that total educational costs have decreased. This, however, was the tactic Hacker used to draw his conclusion in his cost comparison between Medicare and private insurance. If the private insurance industry had similarly reduced its share of health expenses, does Hacker not think that their costs would not also decrease?

And since Medicare has less generous benefits, we can extend the analogy further. If the student were attending a Medicare school, the $10,000 may cover her classes but her room and board would fall outside of tuition, leading to an additional expense. In the private insurance school, more of these expenses would be included in the $10,000 tuition. If we focus on the cost for tuition but do not look at the whole benefit package, we again fail to develop a true apples-to-apples evaluation.

In this more properly aligned comparison we see that total health care spending for Medicare beneficiaries is indeed growing more rapidly than the private sector. This is a very important point. The cost curve is going up more quickly in the segment of the health care industry managed by government. With this being the case, and because it is not occurring as a result of more rapid personal health care costs in the Medicare population as was previously noted, then another question that begs to be asked is, "Why?" Is this occurring as a result of less efficiency, of greater waste, of poor management? To begin, let's evaluate the ability of the public and private sector to efficiently manage their respective health insurance products.

Administrative Costs

I will start this section with a warning: This may be a little (or a lot) boring. I'm sure writing this has to be some kind of faux pas, but hey, this is about administrative costs. One can only spice up a discussion about this topic so much. If this gets too long or tiring, the last three paragraphs under **Administrative Costs: The Insurance Industry** gives the final breakdown comparing Medicare to the private industry and the **Administrative Costs: Making Good Policy** section speaks about the overall findings. But if you are interested in the discussion about single payer, public option or universal health care, then you need to know this information. And I maintain the general notion: The more knowledge, the better.

Broadly defined, health care administrative costs are the expenses incurred that are not directly related to the delivery of a medical service. These include everything from the costs to develop and manage the contracts between insurers and providers, profit, waste, fraud, advertising, claims processing, revenue collection…Everything that does not go out as payment for a health care-related service is counted. The following data will focus on extracting trends with the goal of developing a better sense of how we can shape a more efficient delivery system. This is an attempt to create direct comparisons between the public and private sector.

Two points need to be made before proceeding. First, the goal is to improve efficiency, not necessarily reduce administrative costs to zero. Some of these costs serve important functions—disease management services, minimizing waste and fraud, and nurse consultation hotlines. Second is a citation by Ezra Klein, a journalist for the Washington Post, of an astute quote from Rick Kronick, a former Senior Health Care Policy Advisor in the Clinton administration who has worked extensively on administrative costs in health care.[19] Dr. Kronick noted that "most of the answers to that question [of rising health care costs] have nothing to do with administrative costs. The answers are that we do more stuff and have more technology. Even if we could wring administrative savings out of the system, which I'm all in favor of and would be a good thing, we'd still be facing the question of how to slow the rate of cost growth." I agree. Decreasing these fairly static costs will lower the baseline of the cost curve but not impact its rate of rise. The "we do more stuff" in the quote alludes to a structural issue as the culprit, and this will be addressed later. That said, savings of any type cannot be snubbed and potential cost reduction exists within this facet of our health care delivery system.

Administrative Costs: The Insurance Industry

A portion of the cost of delivering health care rests in the ability of the insurance provider, whether through the private sector or through the government, to maintain an effective delivery system where the dollars that are collected to cover health care expenditures are efficiently used to that end. These costs can be quite difficult to ascertain and as such, generating an apples-to-apples comparison between the government and the private sector ranges from onerous to nearly impossible. While the following information cannot be precise and the appropriateness of some calculations may be questioned, the discussion at least brings important data to the forefront and delineates overall trends, providing a general feel of the true administrative costs. And if we are going to consider altering the supplier of health insurance, we need to determine who can truly deliver it more efficiently. If one sector can direct more of its collected revenue toward covering claims, potential cost savings via reconfiguring the delivery system could then be realized. The following is an attempt to create that direct comparison.

Private industry insurance administrative costs are calculated as:

$$\frac{\text{Premiums collected - claims paid}}{\text{Premiums collected}}$$

For a hypothetical example, if the insurance company collected $100 last year and paid out $85, its administrative costs were 15 percent (100-85/100). This money ($15) has to be used to pay for every aspect of running that insurance company, everything from paying the CEO to the mail clerks, from buying stamps to paying the electricity bill. Everything—it is pretty clean accounting.

While this cost is readily available from the private sector, Medicare's arrangement is quite different. Medicare's administrative costs are calculated by taking the funds appropriated directly to Medicare in the federal budget, and then dividing that amount by the total payments for Medicare beneficiaries:

$$\frac{\text{Federal Budget Expenditures}}{\text{Payment to Beneficiaries}}$$

Using this formula, Medicare's administrative costs have been reported to range from 2.8-3.4 percent. This incredibly low estimate, often referred to during the health care debate as evidence of greater efficiency in government-managed insurance, does not properly depict true administrative costs. Pause for one moment to reflect upon the meaning of these numbers. An administrative cost of 3 percent means that for every dollar that flows to the government for Medicare, 97 cents is returned as payment for patient care. This does not quite pass the common sense "if it's too good to be true, it probably is" test. And it is too good to be true.

Many components of administrative costs are not part of the federal budget directed specifically to Medicare, including:[20]

- Medicare program marketing, outreach and education
- Medicare program customer service
- Medicare program auditing by the Office of the Inspector General
- Medicare program contract negotiation
- Building costs of the Centers for Medicare & Medicaid Services (CMS) dedicated to the Medicare program
- Staff salaries for CMS personnel with Medicare program responsibilities
- Congressional resources exhausted each year on setting Medicare payment rates for services

When these costs incurred through other governmental agencies involved in managing Medicare are added, administrative costs rise to 5.7-6.4 percent.[21]

Before progressing further, breaking administrative costs into three broad categories furthers understanding for later discussion. These costs are attributed to the numerator (the top number) in the above equations.[22]

1. Setting rates and benefits policies: This is a fixed cost for developing the insurance product. This cost does not vary based on utilization of health services or number of beneficiaries.
2. Enrollment, record-keeping and premium collection: This is dependent upon the number of beneficiaries but does not change much based upon utilization of health services.
3. Claims processing: This is dependent upon number of claims submitted; the greater the frequency of utilization of medical services, the greater the cost.

A portion of Medicare's unaccounted costs have been included, and as noted above, the calculation of the administrative costs are currently at

5.7-6.4 percent. However, additional adjustments are still needed to move toward a better direct comparison with the private sector. Administrative costs for claims processing do not vary based on the size of the claim, just on the number of claims. It essentially costs the same to process a $300 claim versus a $3,000 claim. This is done electronically. The larger claim disproportionately increases the denominator in our equation, and this creates the false appearance of lower administrative costs. Since the Medicare population is generally less healthy and has higher medical charges per claim, an adjustment for the average size of claims further increases administrative costs up to 8 percent.[23]

Now most of the appropriate cost adjustments are complete with one great exception—the cost of premium collection. An insurance company cannot exist without collecting funds from its beneficiaries. Again, this is another overlooked cost not attributed to Medicare in previous accountings. The government obtains a majority of premiums through taxation, and these collection expenses are incurred by employers (some Medicare taxes are removed from payroll) as well as the Internal Revenue Service (some are collected through general taxation). However, the cost of taxation extends beyond collection costs. I am not going to delve into the details of the cost to society for tax collection, an unmeasured cost economists refer to as "excess burden" or "dead-weight costs" (please read a great discussion by the Office of Tax Policy Research[24]), but it has been estimated that the societal cost for the federal government to raise one dollar through taxation ranges from 20 to 75 cents.[21,25] In other words, at least 20 cents of every dollar collected is lost in economic activity.

When taking all costs into account, Benjamin Zycher at the Manhattan Institute for Policy Research found that "the lowest plausible assumption about the magnitude of that 'excess burden' of the tax system raises the true cost of delivering Medicare benefits to 24-25 percent of Medicare outlays."[21] This conservative estimate used the figure of 20 percent for excess burden. A separate study in 1994 using a conservative estimate of excess burden came to a similar conclusion, finding that Medicare and Medicaid administrative costs were 26.9 percent.[26] When a midpoint estimate of 50 percent was utilized in Dr. Zycher's study, a number mentioned as a more realistic assumption, Medicare's administrative costs rose to an astounding 52 percent.

As seen previously, calculating the administrative costs for the private industry is less fuzzy. Simply stated, any dollar collected as premium that does not go out as payment for a medical service is considered administrative. For the private industry, this includes the same policy making, enrollment, record-keeping, premium collection and claims processing as seen in the accounting for Medicare. Additional private industry costs not seen in Medicare include increased marketing, profit, claims scrutiny to minimize fraud, state premium taxes (ranging from 1-4 percent, averaging 2 percent), and disease management with nursing hotlines and other efforts intended to improve health.

According to the Congressional Budget Office, the average share of the policy premium that covers administrative costs varies from about 7 percent for employment-based plans with 1,000 or more enrollees to nearly 30 percent for policies purchased by very small firms and individuals.[22] Averaged together, private sector administrative costs have run 12.4 percent over the last 40 years (Source: CMS Office of the Actuary, January 2005). Based on annual company earnings reports from financial year 2009, administrative expenses ranged from 14.8 percent to 18.8 percent for the five major players in the private insurance industry (Wellpoint, Humana, Aetna, United HealthCare, Cigna).

Before bringing the discussion around to a final direct comparison, one additional viewpoint may bring greater clarity to the issue. The administrative costs as discussed thus far are calculated as the expenses for the government and the private sector as a whole. We have evaluated the administrative costs for Medicare and the private industry from more of a global viewpoint, looking at overall industry costs. However, these costs can also be expressed as cost per beneficiary, another method that can further create more of that apples-to-apples comparison. This is particularly relevant in this discussion as it helps remove more of the "numbers play."

Medicare patients, being elderly and generally less healthy, have larger claims, averaging almost twice as much per claim as the private sector. The payout of these claims falls under the denominator (Payment to Beneficiaries), while the cost associated with processing these claims is attributed to the numerator (Federal Budget Expenditures). Nearly all of the cost of claims processing arises from the number of claims, not the expense of each individual claim. As mentioned previously, it does impact cost to process a $300 claim as opposed to a $3,000 claim. If the percentage of Medicare's administrative costs is determined using payments to beneficiaries,

$$\frac{\text{Federal Budget Expenditures}}{\text{Payment to Beneficiaries}}$$

then the denominator in this equation grows more rapidly with greater payouts while the numerator, where the claims processing is attributed, changes little. This leads to artificially low administrative costs—in the reality of this world, writing larger checks does not equate to a more efficient process.

As a substitute for adjusting for this disparity as was done previously, altering the calculation to a cost per-person basis provides another approach to deliver another picture of the administrative cost differences. Now, instead of dividing the governmental expenditures by payments, the expenditures are divided by the number of beneficiaries.

$$\frac{\text{Federal Budget Expenditures}}{\text{Number of Beneficiaries}}$$

The same can be done for the private industry and Figure 2 displays the comparative data.[22] On a per beneficiary basis, Medicare's administrative costs have run anywhere from 5.3 percent to 48.4 percent higher when compared to private insurance over the six year period from 2000 to 2005.

When all appropriate costs are included in the accounting and the playing field is leveled, Medicare is shown to require a higher financial burden to manage. Even using the most conservative estimates, Medicare's overall administrative costs are greater than the private sector's at 24 percent versus 12.4 percent, respectively. And the estimate of Medicare's administrative costs may be as high as 52 percent. As recently as 2009, the highest administrative cost amongst the five major private industry health insurance players was 18.8 percent and was still less than Medicare. And when viewed from the perspective of the cost per beneficiary, the data confirms that Medicare's administrative costs are higher and adds credence to the other studies' findings.

Administrative Costs of Medicare and Private Health Insurance

	Medicare			Private Health Insurance			
Year	Medicare Primary Beneficiaries* (millions)	Total Non-Benefit ("Administrative") Spending** ($billion)	Non-Benefit ("Administrative") Spending per Primary Beneficiary (dollars per person)	Total Beneficiaries† (millions)	Total Non-Benefit ("Administrative") Spending‡ ($billion)	Non-Benefit ("Administrative") Spending per Beneficiary (dollars per person)	Percent by which Medicare Is Higher
2000	37.06	$14.10	$380	202.8	$52.0	$256	48.4%
2001	37.32	14.40	386	201.7	56.6	281	37.5%
2002	37.68	15.84	420	200.9	68.8	342	22.7%
2003	38.11	16.50	433	199.9	82.2	411	5.3%
2004	38.64	20.14	521	200.9	85.3	425	22.7%
2005	39.21	19.94	509	201.2	91.1	453	12.3%

* Derived from CMS Medicare Denominator file and Medicare Enrollment Database. Extract prepared by Susan Y. Hu, Centers for Medicare and Medicaid Services, Office of Research, Development, and Information. Available from the author on request. "Medicare Primary Beneficiaries" excludes those who have another source of coverage (such as employer-sponsored insurance) and are thus subject to the Medicare Second Payer (MSP) rules. Under MSP, Medicare pays only under very limited circumstances and only to the extent, if any, by which Medicare's payment is more generous than the beneficiary's other coverage. Since these individuals derive nearly all of their health benefits from private insurance, they are included as private beneficiaries instead.

** Author's calculations based on Benjamin Zycher, "Comparing Public and Private Health Insurance: Would a Single-Payer System Save Enough to Cover the Uninsured?" Manhattan Institute for Policy Research, October 2007, at http://www.manhattan-institute.org/html/mpr_05.htm (June 25, 2009).

† U.S. Census Bureau, Housing and Household Economic Statistics Division, Current Population Survey.

‡ Centers for Medicare and Medicaid Service, National Health Expenditure Accounts, Table 12, at http://www.cms.hhs.gov/NationalHealthExpendData/downloads/tables.pdf (June 25, 2009).

Table 1 • WM 2505   heritage.org

Figure 2. Administrative Costs of Medicare and Private Health Insurance. Used by permission.

These numbers should make anyone who desires to truly address the cost issue within our health care system take note. If a key goal of health care reform is cost containment and bending the cost curve downward, then expansion of governmental involvement, when evaluated from the perspective of the cost of administering health care dollars in an efficient manner, does not achieve this necessary endpoint. To the contrary, if we shifted a greater portion of management to the federal government, health care costs would certainly increase, potentially to very destructive levels for our economy, accelerating what has been characterized as an unsustainable problem.

And for openness sake, I will reiterate that these costs are difficult to compare. As always, we have to be careful to ensure that we are really bringing about a true apples-to-apples comparison. I have attempted to do this in the discussion. And I have to honestly say, I found this outcome somewhat surprising, especially after continually hearing the "3 percent" Medicare administrative cost number thrown about in the media throughout the health care debate.

Administrative Costs: The Provider Industry

Health care administrative costs do not solely impact the insurance industry. The cost of collecting payment from the insurance agent, whether through the government or private industry, falls upon the provider of the medical service, whether it is a physician, a hospital, an imaging center, and so on. Each of these entities has billing departments that must navigate the intricate rules associated with contracts that lack standardization and vary from one insurer to the next.

For physician's offices, these billing and insurance related expenses have been shown to consume nearly 10-14 percent of revenue at a cost of approximately $85,276 per physician.[28,29] When expressed in total dollar figures, another study estimates the cost at $23 to $31 billion each year.[30] For hospitals, these same expenses were estimated to run between 7-11 percent of revenue based on a 2005 study looking at the cost of health insurance administration in California.[31] When combined, the total billing and insurance-related expenses represent 20-22 percent of revenue for an estimated expenditure approaching $300 billion annually.

This expense has been postulated to result from the complexity of a fragmented, third-party payer system where the billing rules, claims submission forms, and collection processes differ.[32] Each insurer has differing requirements with regard to the authorization process for the utilization of medical services, and each certifies and processes claims differently. This leads to inefficiency and is an area where Medicare has an advantage over the private sector. Medicare covers a large segment of the population without variability in its certification process for the evaluation and treatment of its beneficiaries or its method of claims submission. This homogeneity within Medicare should reduce billing office requirements and thus cost when compared to the private sector.

A 2009 study in the Journal of Oncology Practice reviewed administrative cost differences based on payer mix in 33 hematology-oncology practices distributed amongst diverse localities in 23 states.[33] The study concluded that "practices with a high Medicare payer mix experience both lower mean cost per full time equivalent insurance billing support staff member and total overall insurance billing administrative cost." The findings in this study cannot necessarily be broadly extrapolated to medicine as a whole, as this focused only on the medical specialty of oncology and I could not find other corroborating data.

While a firm conclusion regarding providers' true administrative costs in dealing with either Medicare or the private health insurance industry cannot be definitively drawn, the findings in this study match with common sense and point out the fairly obvious: standardization in billing and collection processes decreases cost. While this should be applied to any reform approach, it does not alter the earlier findings that Medicare's administrative costs greatly exceed the private industry.

Total Administrative Costs

One final approach that attempts to delineate the differences in administrative costs between the private and public sector takes a more global perspective and compares the costs at a national level. This is an attempt to incorporate all aspects of the administrative costs of managing a health care system, and Canada with its single payer system is the obvious model to match against the U.S.

One study from the New England Journal of Medicine published in 1991 compiled the expenses associated with insurance industry overhead, hospital and nursing home administration, and physicians' billing and overhead in the U.S. and Canada. The evaluation based on data from 1987 led the authors to conclude that "health care administration costs between $96.8 billion and $120.4 billion in the United States, amounting to 19.3 to 24.1 percent of total spending on health care. In Canada, between 8.4 and 11.1 percent of health care spending...was devoted to administration."[34] A follow-up study published in 2003 looking at data from 1999 once again concluded that the cost of administering health care was more expensive in the United States, increasing further to 31.0

percent of health care expenditures as opposed to 16.7 percent in Canada.[35]

However, a comprehensive analysis published in Health Affairs in 1992 expanded administrative costs beyond those attributed solely to insurers and health care providers.[36] Patricia Danzon, who holds a doctorate in economics from the University of Chicago, stated "the true 'overhead' of a health insurance system also includes all of the hidden costs associated with financing and operating the insurance and with insurance-induced distortions in the production and consumption of medical care." For example, prolonged waiting times in Canada keep utilization of health care services in check and thus decrease health care costs if viewed solely from the perspective of the insurance industry or the provider. However, patients and society bear these indirect costs in the form of delayed treatment, increased workplace absenteeism and decreased productivity.

A monopolistic, single payer, public health insurance plan's costs are viewed through the prism of budgetary allotment and as such will disregard indirect social costs that do not impact the government's bottom line. This is not a malevolent process, but instead one that is inevitable when incentives to meet patient's needs are distorted in the face of meeting a budget.

Dr. Danzon's study concludes with the statement that "these estimates indicate that costs associated with tax-based financing and rationing [in single payer model] by other than price or information based methods may be at least as great as the parallel costs of premium collection and claims administration incurred by private insurers."

Sorry, not a lot of facts in this section, but this global approach is even more obtuse than trying to tease out administrative costs in Medicare. There are just too many variables to reach a definitive conclusion. That being said, when all societal factors beyond the direct financial accounting are considered, the value of a government-run health insurance system appears to fall well short of the potential that exists in the private sector.

Administrative Costs: Making Good Policy

The data covered previously is an attempt to remove the confounding variables that cloud the true administrative costs of the government and the private sector in order to bring about a more direct comparison. This breakdown is meant to add clarity to a complex topic, and hopefully it has achieved that end. I see no value in numbers play or misleading figures. Our rapidly rising health care costs are an unsustainable problem that needs real solutions, not those driven by misrepresented information or blind ideology. It is only through honest and transparent evaluation that we will begin to understand and acknowledge those inefficiencies, one part of the illness plaguing our system. A disease cannot be cured until it is properly diagnosed. Once we begin to discover those inefficiencies, then we can remove those processes and properly transform our health care system, allowing it to reach its greatest potential. If we otherwise follow our preconceived notions or our politics (which again have no place in medicine), then we will fail, costs will rise, and our society will suffer.

When evaluating the differences in the administrative costs of Medicare compared to the private industry, an area where the data is relatively more robust and accessible, the studies demonstrate that the private sector is more capable of efficiently managing the finances of health insurance. This is true despite the additional cost (and value gained) in the private sector for items such as superior fraud monitoring, nurse hotlines, disease management and educational tools, and so on. Transferring greater control of health care to the federal government would negatively impact the upward bending cost curve, accelerating a currently unsustainable problem—an act that does not represent sound policy steeped in fact and evidence. This conclusion is not drawn from emotion, antigovernment sentiment, or personal feelings, but it is rather the data that uncovers the problems and points to the correct solutions for the issues we face.

That being said, the private industry can learn plenty from the single payer system. Efficiency is more apt to arise out of a uniformity of processes. Standardization of the private health insurance market to include a commonality of contractual language, the development of a single set of procedural rules associated with claims submission, and the utilization of a single claim form are simple ideas that can blossom into other innovations to reduce the burden of billing from the provider's perspective. A study modeling these hypothetical changes predicts a potential annual savings benefit of $7 billion. In addition, physicians will be alleviated of unnecessary administrative tasks that waste an estimated four hours each week, time that can be utilized to care for patients.[28] This will not only reduce unnecessary health care costs that bring no value to patient management, but in an era of decreasing physician availability and increasing time constraints, these changes can add anywhere from 12 to 16 patient visits per week per physician, further increasing health care accessibility.

From the standpoint of health insurance, the McKinsey Global Institute has estimated that 85 percent of excess administrative costs within the private industry arise from product design, underwriting and marketing.[37] Individual experimentation in the design of new insurance products should be promoted rather than hindered, for further efficiencies will come through continued evolution in the health insurance market. I like the idea of competition in this arena—competitiveness breeds efficiency. And while I have no experience in the actuarial realm, I do wonder if potential cost savings could be generated through a uniform underwriting system without impacting the ability of companies to adapt and change. This could maximize efficiency and may also allow smaller insurance companies to come into the marketplace to increase competition.

Profit

This section is included to point out an example where politics promoted noise and demagoguery subverted solutions. Dialogue driven by feigned populist outrage is all too common of an approach by the leaders of our society. Nothing is gained from such actions, yet they often become central to the debate process by those who prefer to redirect the focus on created enemies rather than search out true problems.

The health insurance industry was regularly taken to task, demonized and cast as profiteers throughout the reform debate. Their profits were repeatedly held up as an evil of the system, the cause of skyrocketing health care costs and the reason that so many lacked insurance. Tactics like these stoke public anger, deflect attention and generate emotional responses. However, such commotion diverts us from the task at hand: in this case, finding solutions to the true issues plaguing our health care system.

I am not here to defend, support, accuse or regale the health insurance industry for its profits. That being said, I will honestly say that I am perturbed with the bloated compensation of those who run health insurance companies. But why should I be more bothered with them than I am with sports figures, actors and actresses, musicians, Bill Gates or Warren Buffett or any other group of people or persons who earn exorbitant sums of money? For some of these careers, the salary is based on those things that our society finds valuable, and that is the basis of our capitalistic model, and that is acceptable for me. The real annoyance comes from the cronyism and corporatism that is currently running rampant in our society under the guise of free market capitalism. This leads to decreased competition and the formation of the oligopolies like we see in the health insurance industry (and are now developing in the banking industry where the three largest banks in the U.S. now control 56 percent of the home loans). The ridiculous salaries given to the CEOs of failing institutions like Fannie Mae, Freddie Mac and the Wall Street banks/financial houses along with the health insurance industry CEOs are not commensurate with the value brought to society and extend out of this perverted corporate structure.

But I am here to discuss numbers, data and facts, not our current corporate climate. It is easy to draw knee-jerk conclusions, blindly follow ideological rants (from either side of the political spectrum) and cast dispersions as part of frenzied populism, but rarely is such activity productive. I prefer facts before judgment. I prefer solutions to noise. So what are the facts?

Profit has been covered in a broader sense in the discussion on administrative costs. It is one portion of the difference in premiums collected minus claims paid. As discussed, the data demonstrates that the private sector delivers health insurance in a more cost-effective manner than the federal government. This may occur in spite of profits, but to look on the other side of the coin, perhaps the profits actually drive these companies to work more efficiently (which could be improved even further through increased competition). Perhaps profit is not all bad. For if these companies, despite the added expense of profit, contain costs better than the government, then maybe profit is a positive motivator that minimizes inefficiencies that would otherwise increase administrative costs.

In order to more easily utilize the data from the administrative cost estimates, I will use profit margin in place of profit. Profit margin is calculated as profit per dollar collected in premiums. For example, if a company collects $200 in premiums, pays $150 to beneficiaries for heath care utilization, and uses $40 for overhead expenses, then $10 in profit remains for a profit margin of 5 percent (and administrative cost of 25 percent). If the company collected $1,000 and all of the expenses increased in direct proportion, the profit would be $50 but the profit margin would stay the same. This is the difference between profit and profit margin.

As was noted earlier, administrative costs (overhead plus profit) have averaged 12.4 percent over the last 40 years. Picking out the data from 2009 alone, the highest administrative cost ratio among the top five insurers was 18.8 percent. This caps the maximum profit margin at 18.8 percent (counting all of the administrative costs as profit would assume that no money actually went to managing the company). According to the 2009 Fortune 500 Annual Rankings, the health insurance industry ranked number 35 on the list with a profit margin of 2.2 percent (for perspective, this falls behind other industries that somehow escape the public wrath of profiteering such as food services, gas and electric utilities, electronics, internet services, and beverages). This gives a sensible floor of 2.2 percent and an impractical ceiling of 18.8 percent. I will use HealthSpring, the insurer on the list with the highest profit margin at 5.4 percent, as a measure for profit margin for the entire industry. This choice seems reasonable, maybe even on the high end. But using this higher number at least covers the accounting gimmicks that reduce profit margins on paper that exist in reality (such as exorbitant "business trips" to reward CEOs or salespersons that are expensed to the company).

Based on 2008 data from HHS, the private health insurance industry collected $783.2 billion in premiums. If we take the 5.4 percent profit margin and multiply this by the premiums collected, we get a net profit of $42 billion. To reinforce that this is a high-end figure, the left-leaning Health Care for America Now released a scathing report in February

2010 about the "enjoyed combined profit of $12.2 billion" for the five leading health insurance companies.[38] The estimation of $42 billion in profits is without much doubt greater than reality, but I prefer to err on the side of overestimating cost. This estimate is not an insignificant figure. But again consider that if profit is present in the private industry and not the government, then perhaps it is the variable that leads to the disparity in administrative costs between the two.

To return to the opening point—these insurance industry profits were found contemptible. However, data points to their value. But one aspect of health care costs somehow escaped the politician's wrath, the public outrage and the reform process—medical malpractice lawsuits. How does this compare to these "outrageous" profits? And why is one industry berated while another is ignored?

Medical malpractice for the inappropriately treated patient carries value, but few would argue that multitude of illegitimate lawsuits help society, much less decrease the cost of practicing medicine. The potential for lawsuit lurks in the mind of every physician and often leads to unnecessary testing referred to as defensive medicine.

The exact potential cost savings associated with reforming medical malpractice (tort reform) is debatable. The accounting firm Pricewaterhouse Coopers released a widely critiqued report that concluded that about 10 percent of the cost of medical services is attributable to medical malpractice lawsuits, with roughly 2 percent directly resulting from the costs of lawsuits and an additional 5 percent to 9 percent due to expenses that result from defensive medicine. If this were true, then malpractice reform would save $250 billion in health care costs annually.

On the other side of the spectrum, critics of tort reform discount its value. "It's really just a distraction," said Tom Baker, a professor at the University of Pennsylvania Law School and author of "The Medical Malpractice Myth." "If you were to eliminate medical malpractice liability, even forgetting the negative consequences that would have for safety, accountability, and responsiveness, maybe we'd be talking about 1.5 percent of health care costs. So we're not talking about real money."[39] The "not real money" associated with 1.5 percent of health care expenditures comes to $37.5 billion. According to Leemore Dafny, an economist and expert in healthcare competition who co-authored a research study on medical malpractice reform in the National Bureau of Economic Research Publications, "These costs [of tort reform], all told, have been estimated to be only about 2 percent of healthcare expenses."[40] This pushes the estimated savings to $50 billion.

I suspect the point is obvious. The profits for the health insurance industry that at their highest estimate reach $42 billion (they are likely half of that) have been portrayed as destructive and excessive. On the other hand, the trial lawyers who profit so richly remain unscathed in the debate despite the savings of at least $40 to $50 billion and maybe as much as $200+ billion associated with tort reform. Sadly, the reason is based purely on politics. According to former Democratic National Committee Chairman Howard Dean, "And the reason why tort reform is not in the bill is because the people who wrote it did not want to take on the trial lawyers...And that is the truth."[41]

So is it acceptable to denigrate one industry and discount another despite their comparable impact on the cost of our health care system? Is it appropriate to rally public outcry using half-truths to push an agenda? When this lack of principle and integrity becomes the overriding approach to policy-making, sound decisions based on fact and evidence fall to the wayside. And we as citizens lose.

THE STRUCTURAL ISSUE: MORAL HAZARD AND IMPROPER INCENTIVES

I believe this is the heart of the matter. This is our "disease" and this requires our focus. It is the structure of the system that impairs our ability to contain cost. We can work at the edges, attempting to find ways to minimize administrative costs, to decrease fraud and abuse, and to cut reimbursement to health care providers. We can ration care or curtail medical advancement. We can increase competition, whether through a public option or interstate purchasing of health insurance. We can look to tort reform to decrease unnecessary tests and minimize frivolous lawsuits. We can view health care as a system of unfettered demand with an insufficient supply of dollars, goods and services to meet that demand, a system that can only be limited through price controls or centralized management in order to place a ceiling on expenditures.

While some of these pursuits would undoubtedly decrease a portion of the spending on health care and need to be part of the transformation process, they do not address that which perpetuates the escalating cost. And a few are little more than an attempt to drive a square peg into a round hole. Those who only see these alternatives approach the issue with minimal thought or insight and do not apply problem-solving. These options only see a symptom with little understanding that a disease lies in the background, and a corrective action that treats the symptom and ignores the disease will never cure. Beyond the goal of cost containment, the tradeoffs associated with some of these options are not tenable, much less necessary. Some would impair access or decrease quality. Unless we truly get to the heart of the matter and find that which is driving the costs, the system will still collapse. We may delay the inevitable, but failure will come.

Widening, repaving and repainting a brittle bridge may add to its aesthetics, increase the numbers of people that cross it and make those who use it feel more secure, but in the end, the structure is still weak, and altering the façade only places more at risk when the bridge predictably collapses. The changes mentioned previously do little more than change the aesthetics of health care. Some are helpful and may increase efficiency and decrease cost, but if the underlying system is not addressed, then maximal benefit cannot be reached. So we need to pause, look deeper, and develop a better understanding of the driving forces of health care spending in order to correct those issues that are not allowing our system to function properly.

Before addressing the system, it is necessary to first clarify the goal of health insurance. Is health insurance supposed to protect us from the catastrophic, to decrease the risk of financial collapse as a result of an unexpected illness or injury? Or is health insurance there to provide complete coverage of every health event? This question requires thoughtful examination.

As an example, take a look at auto insurance. Here, we in essence pay for catastrophic coverage—we protect ourselves against the possibility of an accident. Insurance does not pay for gasoline, new tires, oil changes, paint scrapes and door dings. If it did, auto insurance would be exorbitantly expensive. The financial risk for the auto insurance industry would be more difficult to gauge, individuals would lose control over their dollars to manage their own automobiles and cost would escalate as every minor issue would have to pass through the bureaucracy of a third party. Would anyone establish an auto insurance company based on this model? No one has as of yet, and the reason is fairly obvious—it is neither a reasonable nor efficient approach to managing our vehicles.

The risk does not come from the day to day grind on the car but instead arises from the unexpected events. The daily management of the vehicle is predictable and even when some unexpected events occur such as a flat tire or an electrical glitch, the cost is not catastrophic. We expect to cover these expenses ourselves. The auto insurance industry is based upon covering the catastrophic and the unpredictable. Does anyone think they could save money if their daily vehicle costs were rolled into an auto insurance policy? Does anyone think this approach would increase efficiency in the system? While the answers to these questions are obvious, they, for some reason, rarely get asked with regard to our approach to our health care delivery system.

The following is a list of questions that begin to frame the discussion and hopefully focus the thought process on the current arrangement of our health care delivery system and its potential role in the failure to restrain costs. First and foremost—is the structure of the health care delivery system really the problem? Perhaps a better way to ask the question would be: is the system devised to bring about maximal value for the dollar? Is it appropriate for insurance to pay for every office visit, every lab test, every imaging study and every surgery? Is this the most effective economic construct—to pay large sums of money in advance to a third party out of fear of loss only to lose that money if services go unused? And if services are needed, does having a third party who pays the provider for those services establish an appropriate financial relationship to those directly involved in the transaction? Does this type of payment system drive proper incentives to promote appropriate utilization of services by both patients and providers? Are healthy lifestyle choices from patients and cost control from all parties involved demanded or at least promoted in this current system? Does the patient or physician or hospital or imaging center or insurance industry (or government) really have any desire to keep costs and utilization at appropriate levels? Or does the current system separate the cost of a good or service from both the user and provider, thus insulating those involved in the economic transaction of the delivery of health care? Is the model configured such that moral hazard and perverse incentives drive increased utilization and thus increased costs? Are unintended consequences being ignored?

While health care costs are rising, they do not directly affect the users within the system. Patients are paying a small portion of utilization since most health insurance is paid through the employer and employees do not directly see the negative impact upon salary and other benefits that result from rising insurance premiums. They may see incremental changes in the amount of premiums that they cover, but this is still little of the overall cost. Medical device manufacturers and the pharmaceutical industry would prefer more utilization as it drives product consumption. Providers and hospitals are paid on a fee-for-service basis, so they are happy to see more patients and have more admissions. Insurance companies adjust for increased cost by increasing premiums, so they have little motivation to control patient utilization. The government shifts costs, raises taxes or both. So the structure is distorted and the system needs to be better realigned to bring the consumer of the good in more direct control of the cost. If we put more of the costs in the hands of the consumer, then, as is the case in every other industry, the consumer will demand value for the dollar.

Granted, health care is different from other industries. It is one where the knowledge and expertise resides firmly on the side of the providers, but the gap can and needs to be narrowed through greater transparency and education. Perhaps we as a society need to become more educated and enabled consumers of health care rather than using the lack of knowledge as an excuse. A radical change in the delivery of the system is needed, and a radical change in our approach to health care is needed, and this is best achieved by placing the patient as the consumer squarely in the middle of the equation (not that this should be a radical concept). To those who doubt: before jumping to the conclusion that whoever begins to consider such an idea wants to make patients pay for all of their care, please read on. That is the noise creeping in. The following information will hopefully give further insight into this model.

Moral Hazard and 12 Cents on the Dollar

Moral hazard is a term used by economists to define adverse behavioral changes that occur when one is shielded from true risk as a result of alterations in policy, insurance or the law. In financial terms that strike a recent cord, the insidiousness of moral hazard was on display in one facet of our collapsing economy. Fannie Mae and Freddie Mac are mortgage giants that had an implicit guarantee of financial backing from the federal government, meaning the taxpayers. This backing altered the way loan applications were evaluated, for the policy insulated the institutions from the risk of failure. As a result, they supported, purchased or sold the mortgages of people who did not have sufficient collateral to afford their home loans—a business move that would normally be considered quite risky. The executives at Fannie Mae and Freddie Mac would have never allowed this unless they were shielded from the potential of failure. When those homeowners who had obtained loans greater than they could afford were no longer able pay their mortgages, they defaulted, their homes went into foreclosure, and the market collapsed (and Fannie and Freddie have received $145 billion and counting in taxpayer money bail out, and the institutions are still standing and lending—that implicit guarantee was less implicit and more guarantee). The underlying moral hazard drove unnecessary risk-taking that would not have occurred if the institutions were held directly accountable for their practices.

In the realm of health care, moral hazard is postulated to drive over-consumption of medical services and/or promote less healthy behavior as a result of insulating patients from the true cost of health care. The debate about the existence or degree of involvement of moral hazard in medicine has been undertaken by many, and a multitude of studies and essays have come forth on either side of the issue. Before covering this data, I will pass along two analogies to clarify the potential impact of moral hazard on individual health care decisions. One piece of information is necessary to begin this discussion: according to 2008 data from the Organization of Economic Cooperation and Development (OECD), out-of-pocket expenditures in the United States accounted for 12.1 percent of total national health care costs.[42] This means that on average, Americans directly pay 12 cents of every health care dollar. The remaining 88 cents is funded indirectly through lost compensation (via employer-sponsored insurance) and taxation, two methods of revenue collection that hide the true costs from those who use the system.

Let's take this number of 12 cents and look at a non-health care scenario. Frank is shopping for a car. He has $5,000 to spend, and he begins to shop around. When he gets to the dealer, he discovers that he only has to pay 12 cents on the dollar. His $5,000 has suddenly become $42,000, with the difference covered by some other third party. So the question is, does Frank opt to buy the used Ford or does he purchase a brand new Mercedes? What would you do? Most would buy the Mercedes, especially when you get it for the price of the Ford. And from the dealer's perspective, he would rather get paid the $42,000, so what is he going to encourage Frank to buy? And when Joan walks in, what is the dealer going to push her to buy? There is no incentive from either party to be frugal, for the consumer is insulated from the additional $37,000 in the transaction and the provider makes more money selling the expensive automobile. But the hazard does not stop there. Once the car is purchased, is it as valuable to the consumer? Not really—its value is $5,000, not the $42,000 that it truly cost. So is the incentive to manage the car properly, to change the oil, to minimize wear and tear as strong as if the full price were paid? Of course not. Frank could buy a new Mercedes again for only $5,000, so he does not take care of the car nearly as well. And in this scenario, what would happen to the overall expenditures on automobiles? They would sky rocket.

How does this play out in health care? Let's turn to Mike. He is 45, works hard and is married with two children. He has "good" health insurance in that he pays $10 to see his physician and has to pay $10 for his prescriptions (he only pays 12 cents on every dollar of cost). He has a fairly sedentary job, is a meat and potatoes kind of guy who eats poorly during the day, snacks on chips and soda, gets home and consumes more than necessary for dinner, enjoys his cookies for dessert and drinks a few beers while catching a ballgame on TV before going to bed. His idea of exercise is walking from his car to the office and from his desk to the copier. He's a little overweight and badly out of shape. He goes to see his family doctor whom he sees annually, more often if necessary. Mike has a family history of heart disease and his cholesterol is rising. He is told that he must exercise and eat better, and his doctor starts him on a cholesterol-lowering medication.

Many factors will play into Mike's decision-making process, but the moral hazard within the system will undoubtedly affect his choice. He finds it easier to take the pill—it keeps his cholesterol low, he does not have to change those things that he finds enjoyable, and he only pays a few dollars for the medication. Sure, he will now have to go to the doctor's office every three months instead of annually for blood tests, but hey, it's still only a few bucks out of his pocket. He is removed from a majority of the additional cost to the health care system that his lifestyle choice has created—four times as many office visits, a new medication and frequent lab testing. This is not to say that he does not pay for this care: he is just less aware of how his choice has increased the silent 88 cents that he never sees. The financial incentive to eat healthy, work out, get off the medication and see his doctor less often is removed. Joining a gym would actually raise his personal expenditures since a majority of his current medical costs are covered through a third party. He gets to have his cake and eat it too...life is good. And health care expenditures go up. And worse yet, Mike is still unhealthy; his numbers just look a little better—for now.

Does this occur in medicine, or is this story a misrepresentation of our health system and society? First, look around and see what your friends and colleagues are doing? Then self-evaluate—how do you personally respond to the request of your physician to eat better and exercise more? And then consider why so many do not manage their health properly or follow preventive medicine. Is this plain old apathy, or is there something deeper, something more sinister like moral hazard subtly altering behavior? Let's turn to the data and then the arguments.

I am going to focus on a single aspect of health—obesity—and see what studies have discovered with regard to this problem in our society and its relationship to health insurance and moral hazard. Why obesity? Aside from the financial impact, which will be discussed, this is generally a self-inflicted condition that can be avoided through proper self management. It is a point of attack for our health care system, especially amongst those who advocate health. Childhood obesity has become the platform of our First Lady Michelle Obama.

Aside from the impact of obesity on individuals, its cost spreads to the rest of society. An article in Health Affairs in 2004 found that the obesity epidemic accounted for 27 percent of the growth in inflation-adjusted health care spending in the United States from 1987 to 2001.[43] A 2005 study estimated that the federal government pays for roughly half of the total annual medical costs associated with obesity, resulting in an average annual increase of $175 in everyone's taxes to pay for obesity expenditures among Medicaid and Medicare recipients.[44] A study in Health Affairs in June 2009 revealed that the medical costs of obesity in the U.S. rose from an estimated $78.5 billion in 1998 to $147 billion in 2008, a time during which the prevalence of obesity rose 37 percent. The medical costs for an obese person are 42 percent higher than a person of normal weight, equating to an additional $1,429 per year.[45]

I doubt this information covering the cost impact of obesity is surprising. Obesity is associated with diabetes, high blood pressure, heart disease, hormonal abnormalities, degenerative joint disease, increased cancer risk and so on. The example of obesity was not chosen to deride one segment of society but rather to look for evidence of moral hazard in an issue that can act as a surrogate for other unhealthy lifestyle choices. And again, beyond the cost issue, I am one of those physicians who advocate health. I see the ravages of obesity on our bodies and its impact upon the quality of life of my patients. If the undercurrent of moral hazard within our system is inhibiting proper lifestyle choices, then it is imperative that we address this issue and change the system. This necessary to not only to control costs, but it is necessary because we are maintaining a system that causes harm.

So what does health insurance have to do with obesity and moral hazard? One interesting paper published by the National Bureau of Economic Research in July 2009 drew the following conclusions as discussed by its author:

"Americans who have health insurance, either private or public, are more likely to gain weight or become obese...According to the paper, which estimates weight gain in terms of body mass index, a measure of weight related to height, private insurance increases BMI by 1.3 points and public insurance increases BMI by 2.1 points." [16]

"Our results indicate that health insurance does indeed make you fat...Our estimates suggest that, by insulating people from the cost of obesity-related medical expenditures, insurance coverage creates moral hazard in behaviors related to body weight. These effects are larger in the public insurance programs where premiums are not risk adjusted and smaller in private insurance markets where the obese might pay for incremental medical care costs in the form of lower wages. ...these findings indicate that providing incentives for healthy behaviors, especially among those with public coverage, might improve social welfare." [17]

The impact of health insurance and obesity was further elucidated by Jay Bhattacharya of Stanford University and Neeraj Sood of the RAND Corporation. The authors found that when health insurers do not adjust premiums based on weight, people have a tendency to be heavier and thus less healthy.[48] This finding was based upon a similar modeling of health insurance and what has been described as a "measure of self-protection" as expressed in a seminal paper by Erhlich and Becker in 1972.[49] According to the authors, "On the one hand, self protection is discouraged because its marginal gain is reduced by the reduction of the difference between the incomes and thus the utilities in different states, on the other hand, it is encouraged if the price of market insurance is negatively related to the amount spent on protection through the effect of these expenditures on the probabilities." This translates to the simple idea that healthy behavior (the measure of self-protection) increases if the gain positively correlates with the cost. On the other hand, if this measure of self-protection is removed through separating the risk from the true cost, then healthy activity is disincented. "Self-protection would then usually be discouraged by market insurance–moral hazard would exist–because the main effect of introducing market insurance would be to narrow the differences between incomes in different states." This statement reiterates the negative impact of moral hazard that develops as people are insulated from the cost of their lifestyle decisions. Obesity is the undesirable behavioral change that occurs as a result of insurance, particularly as it relates to the current structure of our health care system.

These studies are not meant to ascribe the moral hazard associated with health insurance as the sole cause of the rapid growth of obesity within our society. That would undoubtedly be a simplistic view of a complex problem. However, the data does bring insight to what may be one of the drivers of the growing obesity epidemic in America.

More importantly, if we identify moral hazard in the structure of the system promoting the poor lifestyle choice of obesity, then we can extrapolate that trend across preventive medicine in general. A multitude of studies and papers have identified the impact of insurance on moral hazard in other aspects of health. If we can find any way, even small ways, to combat and diminish moral hazard's negative effects, then we as a society will be healthier and health care costs will fall. Imagine the savings that can come from reform that finds a way to effectively alter the mindset of our society toward a focus on health—$149 billion is waiting to be trimmed with weight loss alone. We need to cure the disease of moral hazard impacting our system rather than managing the symptoms. It is easier to choose the proper treatment when the correct diagnosis is made.

The argument against the validity of moral hazard's existence within the health care system has been covered in many articles. The authors of such papers generally argue that health care consumption does not follow the same economic rules as other industries with regard to moral hazard. The reason: people only grudgingly visit the doctor when ill. Few enjoy having to wear odd paper gowns and be poked and prodded. Since this is the case, rarely would anyone increase medical utilization as a result of insulation from the cost of the service. As Princeton economist Uwe Reinhardt says, "Moral hazard is overblown. You always hear that the demand for health care is unlimited. This is just not true. People who are very well insured, who are very rich, do you see them check into the hospital because it's free? Do people really like to go to the doctor? Do they check into the hospital instead of playing golf?"

This is one common theme of the arguments made against the impact of moral hazard on health care utilization. And while on the surface it seems to carry some validity, the statement does not get to the depth of the effects of moral hazard. Are people going to voluntarily subject themselves to the generally accepted unpleasantness of increased medical intervention? Of course not. But does the invisible hand of moral hazard alter human behavior and thus portend this outcome? The data points to this as being true.

Let's return to fictional Mike for a second. He is our prior patient example who was placed on a cholesterol-lowering medication that increases his office follow-up to every three months instead of annually. Mike is not consciously making a choice to use more health care services and see his doctor four times as often. However, his choice of a less healthy lifestyle has brought about higher cholesterol levels. This has led his physician to add a cholesterol-lowering agent to his medical regimen which in turn has led to an increase in office visits since adding this new medication brings about additional health risks.

While the data points to a lifestyle partly influenced by moral hazard, his subsequent decision-making process to deal with the effects of this choice is impacted as well. He will opt to continue a higher risk lifestyle as a result of being insulated from the outcome of that choice. Mike is buffered from a majority of the rising cost of his health care, and his incentive to eat better, exercise and lose weight is diminished. So no, Mike did not wake up and tell himself that he is going to visit the doctor more often since he has to pay only a small portion of his medical expense. He is not passing on a chance to play golf or bowl with friends just so that he can go through an awkward experience more frequently. That is too simplistic of a thought process. He has instead moved down a path of moral hazard, and whether done consciously or subconsciously, his decisions have increased his use of medical services. The slippery slope of moral hazard and its impact on decision-making cannot be underestimated. If we ignore the subtle motivations that alter human behavior and hastily dismiss the unintended consequences of policy, then we will lose potential pieces that may fit into effective reform of the health care system.

Cost Sharing

"In normal markets, demand is modulated by cost. But the third-party payment for patients attenuates this control. Although patients experience deductibles, co-payments, and other out-of-pocket expenses, health insurance and government programs significantly shield patients' decisions from the true costs of health care."[50]

Ezekiel Emanuel, MD, PhD JAMA June 18, 2008

Cost sharing is the financial contribution for the utilization of health care services borne by the patient above the amount paid by the insurer and includes:

- copayments (a flat amount per service, i.e. the $40 paid at the time of the office visit)
- coinsurance (a percentage of the charge that the consumer must pay)
- deductibles (annual out-of-pocket expense that must be met before coverage begins)

Health insurance plans that fall under the increased cost sharing approach are called high deductible health plans (HDHPs) or consumer-driven health plans (CDHPs). These plans require the beneficiary to cover the cost of their care until the higher deductible is met, although a greater number of insurers are providing first dollar coverage of preventive medicine. The cost of additional care is then shared between the insurance company and the beneficiary until the maximum out-of-pocket expenses are reached, at which time the insurer covers any additional expenditures.

The premiums for the CDHPs are less than the traditional comprehensive plans. They are also associated with a medical savings account, an account in which money can be placed in a tax-free manner, and these funds are used to help cover the cost of care. However, if the account is used in full to cover medical expenses, then the patient must cover the remaining health care costs without the benefit of tax deductibility until the maximum out of pocket expenditure is reached. The health savings account (HSA) is a common form of these accounts and is one where the money accrues interest over time. Any unused funds remain with the policy holder, are portable and roll over from year to year, growing in value over time.

The HDHPs with the HSAs only recently came to the market as part of the Medicare Prescription Drug and Modernization Act of 2003. Since the idea is based around placing the patient as the consumer in greater control of their health care dollars, the overall approach of CDHPs and HSAs is one component of what is referred to as health care consumerism.

This plan structure runs contrary to traditional insurance. In the traditional model, patient cost sharing is minimized with lower deductibles, co-pays and out-of-pocket expenditures. Patients are held less directly accountable for the cost of medical services (12 cents on the dollar)—the plans are more comprehensive and the beneficiaries are insulated from the cost of care. However, the premiums associated with these plans are higher. The insurance company, whether the government or the private industry, collects and manages all health care dollars, distributing the funds to providers based on beneficiary utilization. If the beneficiary does not engage the health care system, then the excess from the premium is used to manage others' costs within the insured cohort. The money is not retained by the beneficiary for the following year.

The discussion regarding moral hazard is based around the appropriateness of cost sharing, and this has been a hot topic with regard to health care reform. Supporters of increased cost sharing and health care consumerism argue that this approach will discourage the use of unnecessary health care services. In addition, since patients carry a greater cost burden, they are more likely to choose healthier lifestyles and manage their chronic health conditions better. When medical care is required, patients would be more likely to shop around for the least costly alternative while carrying higher expectations of value for their dollar. Insurance is then utilized to minimize the cost of chronic disease or to cover those unpredictable expenses of accidents or acute illnesses.

Relating this to the previously outlined auto example, we change the oil in our cars as a preventive measure to minimize the likelihood that the engine will break down. We do this because maintaining proper care decreases our costs in the long run (since we pay as opposed to some third party). When the car does succumb to the wear and tear of use, we shop around to find the mechanic who completes the repairs effectively and at the best price. If we are involved in an accident, then our insurance kicks in to help guard against catastrophic expenditures.

The goal of such an approach is to raise the level of health in a society while decreasing cost. This is accomplished by maximizing the patient's direct involvement in their health and placing the responsibility for the outcomes that arise from personal lifestyle choices upon the individual. The patient becomes the consumer at the center of the health care model, moral hazard is minimized, and the system becomes more in line with basic economic principles.

The argument against cost sharing is that it discourages people from using health care (which may worsen a condition and lead to more expensive care), it shifts greater costs onto patients, and it is inequitable for the low income, the unemployed, and those with considerable health care costs who end up paying a higher percentage of their salary to cover health-related expenses.[51] Others also argue that the uninsured do not pay high enough marginal tax rates to substantially benefit from the tax deductibility of the HSAs and will therefore see little benefit from paying into these accounts. Enactment of reform based on these plans would therefore have minimal effect on increasing coverage. To the contrary, some fear that these plans may in fact destabilize the insurance market-place by selecting out the young, healthy and wealthy while leaving the remaining higher risk population in plans that would then become increasingly expensive.[52,53,54]

As is the theme thus far, let us turn to the data to better parse the arguments, quiet the noise and search out truth. The RAND Corporation conducted the landmark Health Insurance Experiment (HIE) from 1971 to 1982.[55] In this experiment, 2,750 families composed of 7,700 individuals were randomly assigned to different cost-sharing insurance plans for a period of three to five years. These plans followed a graduated model, beginning with free care and then increasing cost sharing from 25 percent to 50 percent to 95 percent (similar to the HDHPs). The amount of cost sharing was income-adjusted, and the out-of-pocket expenses were capped according to income.

The researchers then looked at health care utilization, expenditures and quality of care. The researchers found that higher cost sharing reduced the use of nearly all health services and as such led to a decrease in health care expenditures. The participants in each cost sharing group spent less than the free care pool. Most importantly, this reduction in utilization and expenditures did not adversely affect outcomes on the great majority of participant's health. The one exception occurred in the lower income, high health risk population: the health in this subgroup was negatively impacted with greater cost sharing.

A wonderful, apolitical evaluation of this study was written for the Kaiser Family Foundation by Dr. Jonathan Gruber, an economist at the Massachusetts Institute of Technology.

"In summary, the lessons from the HIE are very clear: higher co-insurance rates, with an out-of-pocket limit, can significantly reduce health care use without sacrificing health outcomes for the typical person. The results are surprisingly robust and hold across many sub-samples of the data: rich and poor, sick and healthy, adult and child. The one clear negative impact on health occurs only for those who are at high

medical risk, particularly if they are also of lower income. This effect, while not statistically significant, is very large, and suggests the value of considering targeted co-insurance approaches that minimize the costs to this group." [56]

The transferability of the results of this study from the early 1980's into today's health care debate is questionable, but patterns of behavior can be extrapolated. The study demonstrated that increasing cost sharing did indeed decrease utilization and thus cost without negatively impacting health for the average participant. The experiment also demonstrated that while those in the higher cost sharing plans spent less on health care (the 95 percent cost sharing group realized 30 percent in savings compared to the free care group), the savings unfortunately did not come from patients shopping around for the cheapest price but instead came from using fewer services. These participants did not become more frugal shoppers; they just shopped less often. Finally, the experiment examined whether those who carried a greater share of cost led healthier lifestyles and found that the rate of unhealthy choices such as smoking and obesity were unaffected.

So while savings were realized, they did not occur as a result of patients taking a more discerning approach to the cost of care or by living healthier. As such, the savings associated with increased cost sharing would be realized at the initiation of the plan while the rise in health care expenditures would continue at the same rate. Based on this experiment, cost sharing would help decrease cost, but it is not the solution to the structural issue of our health care system. Basically, the cost curve would follow its current trajectory but would start at a lower point.

However, more recent studies have looked into the impact of increased cost sharing in today's society. In May 2009, The American Academy of Actuaries evaluated emerging data on high deductible health plans (HDHPs). [57] The studies used control groups to minimize selection bias in the data. The Academy found that within the first year, implementation of HDHPs led to a decrease in cost trends ranging from 4 percent to 15 percent versus traditional plans that experienced cost increases of 8 percent to 9 percent. Taken together, this data demonstrated that companies using HDHPs generated savings anywhere from 12 percent to 20 percent in the first year. Beyond the initial year, two studies indicated a 3 percent to 5 percent lower trend line in cost compared to the traditional plans. One of the evaluated studies, the Aetna HealthFund report, found that over a six-year period, employers who switched to an HDHP sustained decreases in health care costs of $21 million per 10,000 employees.[58] These findings are extremely valuable, for they finally demonstrate not only a decrease in health care expenditures, but they also point to a potential model that can actually bend the cost curve downward.

An equally substantial finding was noted: the cost savings did not come from avoidance of appropriate care. To the contrary, beneficiaries of these plans were noted to have a 4 percent to 23 percent increase in preventive services. The participants also received recommended care for chronic illnesses at the same or higher level than the plans with less cost sharing. Health information and cost of care tools were utilized more frequently as the participants became more educated consumers.

We are now beginning to see not only a one-time decrease in expenditures, but a decrease in the rate of health care spending as well. And this is occurring along with increased use of preventive services and proper management of chronic illness. The studies established control groups to account for differing levels of health status to remove selection bias as the cause for the cost improvement. The actuarial report concluded, "If these lower trends can be further validated, it will represent a substantial cost-reduction strategy for employers and employees."

When evaluating cost sharing from the viewpoint of the critics, this data should appease some of their concerns. Even those who approach cost sharing with a level of disdain have to appreciate the potential cost savings and the downward bending of the cost curve associated with these plans. And the studies demonstrated that health care costs did not decrease as a result of missing appropriate care. To the contrary, utilization of preventive services and management of chronic health conditions improved. The shifting of cost onto patients was not addressed in the analysis, but with the decrease in the employer's premium costs associated with these plans, they are frequently contributing into the employee's HSAs. Additional options to further decrease patient cost through work-place incentives will be discussed later, and legislation can be put in place to allow insurance companies themselves to pay into their beneficiaries' accounts if they meet certain health-based criteria. The reasoning: for the employer, a healthier employee is more productive at work; and for the insurance company, a healthier beneficiary is less likely to reach the deductible. Other concerns regarding the lack of tax deductibility for those who do not pay taxes (the working poor) can be easily alleviated by standardizing the tax deductibility and even providing a refundable tax credit.

While the detractors will continue to punch holes in this approach, its value in decreasing cost and altering our unsustainable cost trajectory without negatively impacting care is evident. As for those who argue for less cost sharing, a CBO report from December 2008 concluded that total spending would be greater under health reform proposals that reduce cost sharing (follow the comprehensive approach to insurance) and calculated that a 10 percent decrease in enrollees' out-of-pocket costs would typically cause average spending on health care to increase by 1 percent to 2 percent.[27] This finding was evident in the RAND experiment. Health care expenditures were inversely related to the level of cost sharing—the least cost sharing free care pool spent the most, while the 95 percent cost sharing pool spent the least.

So are HDHPs and HSAs perfect? No, the model needs work, and the nuances of plan implementation to offset all of the critics' worries fall beyond the scope of this book. But from the global perspective, I see value. I see a framework forming that can be modified to reach its full potential. As opposed to just repainting the bridge, it is now being rebuilt. A major structural issue, the moral hazard imbedded in our current health care system, is diminished. The structure of the health care system is more properly aligned, the consumer is directly involved in the exchange of cost for the service provided, and the value of health is increased. These positive effects can be augmented with further adaptation, and the correction of misaligned incentives to be discussed in the following section will present additional methods to maximize the efficacy of this model. Health care consumerism as a viable approach to transform the health care system into a more efficient, less costly model is emerging. And it is data, not ideology or noise, leading the way.

Incentivization

"Many people have difficulty changing health behaviors because it requires trade-offs between immediate consumption and delayed and often intangible health benefits. Incentives can provide people with immediate and tangible feedback that helps make it easier for them to do in the short term what is in their long-term best interest."[59]

Janet Weiner, MPH, Associate Director for Health Policy
Leonard Davis Institute of Health Economics, University of Pennsylvania

Addressing incentives is a necessary adjunct to the minimization of moral hazard. Any discussion that focuses on cost sharing without considering the benefits of properly aligned incentives and their impact on human behavior will miss the potential gains brought about by this combination. If incentives are not tied to reducing the moral hazard imbedded in health insurance, then cost sharing is less apt to achieve its maximal benefit. The following are excerpts from those who argue against the potential value brought about through diminishing the effect of moral hazard in our health care system.

Malcolm Gladwell, in a piece in the New Yorker in 2005 wrote, "Health Savings Accounts represent the final, irrevocable step in the actuarial direction (insurance pricing based on personal risk, not shared risk). If you are preoccupied with moral hazard, then you want people to pay for care with their own money, and, when you do that, the sick inevitably end up paying more than the healthy... Do you think that people whose genes predispose them to depression or cancer, or whose poverty complicates asthma or diabetes, or who get hit by a drunk driver, or who have to keep their mouths closed because their teeth are rotting ought to bear a greater share of the costs of their health care than those of us who are lucky enough to escape such misfortunes?"[60]

Economist Paul Krugman has written about the 80-20 rule associated with medical expenditures. In 2003, studies found that eighty percent of all health care costs arose from twenty percent of the population. The underlying premise of Krugman's assertions is that the great majority of the cost of medical care arises from a fixed group with unavoidable illness, a group predisposed to increased medical intervention as opposed to those who increase utilization as a result of the insidious effect of moral hazard on personal health. With that being the case, nothing positive can be done to alter the cost trajectory of this segment of the population. They are constrained by fate without potential for salvation to a life of illness, unremitting medical care and exorbitant health care expenditures.

An Issue Brief put forth by Mathematica Policy Research, Inc. concludes that "financial incentives [increased cost sharing] may not significantly change the overall costs of care. Consumers with serious health problems account for most health care costs. Even if strong incentives induce these consumers to use care judiciously, most of their care is nondiscretionary."[61]

The problem with these arguments and the many similar to them is that they view the problems impacting our system through tunneled vision, missing the interplay of factors that can work synergistically to impact not only cost but health. They in essence see a constellation of distinct symptoms but miss the underlying disease and then conclude that the disease is incurable.

The goal of increased cost sharing is to reduce the moral hazard associated with the buffering of risk that arises from health insurance. But the ultimate goal of the transformation of our health care is to develop a system that not only decreases expenditures but also promotes a healthier society. The previously discussed data points to the ability of increased cost sharing to alter the underlying structure of our health care delivery system to begin to lay a framework that builds toward that end. However, the carrot (or stick) of proper incentives could be used as an adjunct to create a culture of health. People would not only be motivated to monitor their personal expenditures to save money since they have greater control over their health care dollars, but they would also receive rewards (or punishment) that encourage healthy lifestyle choices. By applying these two concepts in tandem, perhaps we can create a healthier society that requires less medical intervention, a healthier society that is more productive and a healthier society that truly bends the cost curve downward.

The objective of true reform is the elimination of the moral hazard and the alteration of the improper incentives that increase the prevalence of chronic conditions that arise not out of bad luck or genetics, but those that arise out of unhealthy lifestyle choices. A second aim of this transformation extends to those predisposed conditions: improved management of illnesses based upon similar motivational changes that can follow removal of the perverse effects of these two factors. Unlike Victor Fuchs, MA, PhD, professor of economics and of health research and policy, who stated, "I do not believe that increased cost sharing is a way to reduce the social redistributive element of insurance", I view the data from a different perspective. Increased cost sharing is a way to reduce the social and personal cost of the moral hazard that subtly subverts the value of healthy living and as such worsens the health of the members of our society. Perhaps weakening the social redistributive element of health insurance is a good thing that can be used to not only decrease cost but also alter poor lifestyle choices that diminish the quality of life of our fellow citizens. The extent of sickness in our society is a symptom. Solely focusing on the symptom while ignoring the underlying disease in the construct of our health care system that promotes this symptom will preclude any potential to develop a cure.

For what do we know about healthy versus unhealthy living in our society? We know that 70 percent of diseases are based on lifestyle choices. Diabetes, hypertension, heart and vascular disease, obesity, cancer—sure some of these occur as a result of a genetic predisposition, but the majority arises from those factors that we can directly impact. For example, according the Centers for Disease Control and Prevention, about 90 percent of lung cancer deaths in men and almost 80 percent of lung cancer deaths in women in the United States are due to smoking.[2] People who smoke are 10 to 20 times more likely to get lung cancer or die from lung cancer than people who do not smoke. Furthermore, 80 percent of cardiovascular disease and diabetes, 60 percent of cancers and more than 90 percent of obesity is preventable. I could pull data set after data set that relates similar information correlating unhealthy lifestyle choices to the disease processes listed above, but most understand the correlation between unhealthy living and the increased risk for disease. These findings readily illustrate my point, for these are symptoms of the disease that needs to be remedied.

Cancer or illness will strike those who eat well and exercise and do all of the right things. The cost of treatment for this group is a constant and likely one that cannot be broadly impacted through alteration in the structure of our health care system. But I, and many physicians, also see obese patients who smoke and do not exercise and eat poorly and continue to follow these poor choices despite ongoing advice to alter behavior. So the real question is: How many of those people in the 20 percent that utilize 80 percent of health care resources do so out of bad luck, bad genes, and bad karma and how many do so because they have made poor lifestyle choices that then lead to poor health that then leads to increased expenditures? How many in that expensive and sick 20 percent result from the 70 percent of preventable disease? And why is this problem glossed over or portrayed as unalterable, incurable?

I disagree with those who say that we cannot impact health care expenditures because sick people are going to be sick. By accepting this thought, we then condemn our society to an unnecessary burden of disease. Let's stop resigning ourselves to this extent of disease prevalence or worse yet promoting it through moral hazard and improper incentives, dismissively shrugging our shoulders as costs continue to spiral and the health of those in our society progressively deteriorates. Perhaps if we became less reactive and instead began to proactively look at ways to decrease the percentage of our society that is obese, that has hypertension or diabetes or heart disease or cancer, we then would add another tool to further impact costs and add to the quality of life. Maybe we can alter that 20 percent, decrease that 20 percent, make the illnesses in that 20 percent less severe and more apt to respond to therapy. This seems more reasonable. Actually, this seems more humane and more caring.

Many will say that prevention has been discussed ad nauseum, and many have tried to alter behavior and promote healthier lifestyles. True, but these attempts have been undertaken within a broken system of perverse incentives and moral hazard, and it has predictably failed. But imagine how much we could save if no one smoked, if we ate well, if we exercised...if we created a culture of health. Should we just place the lung cancer patient into the category of the 20 percent that use 80 percent of health care resources, or should we strive to find ways to alter destructive behavior? Is this even possible, or do we just have to accept the inevitable level of illness and health care utilization that Paul Krugman and Malcolm Gladwell and a multitude of others express as unalterable. Is thinking otherwise just fanciful?

The previously presented data regarding the relationship between health insurance and obesity begins to demonstrate the effect of the moral hazard within our system. Another study in the Journal of Law and Economics evaluated the potential of a rise in mandated coverage of the medical treatment of diabetes "to generate a moral hazard to the extent that medical treatments might displace individual behavioral improvements." The conclusion: "We find that mandates do generate a moral hazard problem with diabetics exhibiting higher BMIs after the adoption of these mandates."[63] To go on: the Geneva Papers on Risk and Insurance used data from the U.S. Panel Study of Income Dynamics (1999–2003) to evaluate the impact of insurance coverage on four lifestyle decisions: heavy smoking, heavy drinking, lack of exercise and obesity. Their findings: "Health insurance has significant incentive effects on lifestyle choices, increasing the propensity to heavy smoking, lack of exercise and obesity and decreasing the propensity to heavy drinking.[64] So we again see the impact of the moral hazard on health behavior and are thus presented with a potential point of attack to positively impact the cost side of the health care cost equation. But what about incentives? Do we have evidence that we can additionally impact behavior through proper incentivization to further drive down cost while improving health?

A Congressional Office Report from November 2007 titled The Long-Term Outlook for Health Care Spending stated:

Two potentially complementary approaches to reducing spending on Medicare, Medicaid, and health care generally—rather than simply reallocating spending among different sectors of the economy—involve ...changing the incentives for providers and consumers in the supply and demand of health care...The current financial incentives facing both providers and patients tend to encourage or at least facilitate the adoption of expensive treatments and procedures...Even in the absence of more information about comparative effectiveness, changes in incentives could help to control health care costs...[65]

Studies have cemented the value of incentives in improving healthy behavior. An Issue Brief from the Leonard Davis Institute of Health Economics from the University of Pennsylvania's Center for Health Incentives looked at two studies focusing on the impact of financial incentives in the area of smoking cessation and weight loss.[66] For tobacco use, they found that the incentive group achieved significantly higher quit rates than the control group in both the short-term and long-term. The authors of this study, published in the New England Journal of Medicine in February 2009, stated, "In this study of employees of one large company, financial incentives for smoking cessation significantly increased the rates of smoking cessation."[67] For the weight loss cohort, participants in the two incentive groups lost significantly more weight than those in the control group during the first 16 weeks of the study. The differences in weight loss narrowed when incentives were discontinued, and while the differences were no longer statistically significant after seven months, net weight loss remained larger in the incentive groups compared to the control group by more than a two to one margin. I could again pull innumerable studies that discuss the effects of incentives upon altering health behavior—most agree with their positive effect and generally only differ in the extent and duration of that effect.

The concept of incentivizing people to live healthier lives as a way to reduce costs was put on trial by the grocery store chain Safeway, Inc. in a real world model where we move beyond pontification and ideas and obtain salient data. Safeway, like a great majority of businesses in the U.S., was struggling to deal with rising health care costs. Expenditures were growing at an annual rate of 10 percent. Beginning in 2005, the company replaced its health care plan with one that was based upon personal choice and responsibility. The company's executives developed a health care consumerism approach to their problem. Under the new plan, the company deposited $1,000 each year into a "health reimbursement account," which workers could use to pay for care. The next $1,000 in expenses was the employee's responsibility. After that, employees paid 20 percent of costs up to a $4,000 maximum. This portion of the plan focused on minimizing the moral hazard associated with limited cost sharing.

The employees who enrolled in the new plan were tested in four areas: smoking, body mass index, blood pressure and cholesterol. For each area where the employee reached set health-based goals, they received a reduction in their premium, reaching as much as $1,560 for a family per year. Those who failed to reach the criteria but showed progress could get refunds. This was obviously the incentive portion.

Safeway complemented this with an intense culture of health ranging from weight-loss tips and fitness competitions to smoking cessation programs. This extended the plan to develop a culture of health, part of the expanded approach of health care consumerism. The plan impacted nearly 75 percent of its nonunion workforce. According to company CEO Stephen Burd,

"The results have been remarkable. During this four-year period, we have kept our per capita health-care costs flat (that includes both the employee and the employer portion), while most American companies' costs have increased 38 percent over the same four years."[68]

Safeway's Senior Vice President Ken Shachmut who oversees the health care program reiterated,

"This is the silver lining in the cloud of rising health costs. If we can design incentives in these core areas, we have a fighting chance of getting our arms around it."[69]

Some have argued that the cost savings as put forth by Mr. Burd are misleading.[70] While time will test the veracity of cost savings, maintaining a program that increases cost would seem counterproductive for a private company that needs to earn a profit to compete in the marketplace. However, the cost savings were only one benefit this program delivered to the participants. The second round of wellness testing demonstrated a slate of positive health results that should not be dismissed:[70]

- the proportion of employees classified as obese fell 5 percent
- the portion of those previously described as overweight fell 1 percent
- 40 percent who previously failed the blood pressure criterion passed
- 30 percent of former smokers registered as tobacco-free
- 17 percent who previously failed the cholesterol test passed

Many other corporations have been following workplace incentivization programs to good effect. Johnson & Johnson established a program in 1979 and it has realized cost savings of $250 million over the last ten years. According to spokesperson Carol Goodwrich, "Through a combination of programs that includes a health risk assessment, lifestyle and disease management counseling, risk intervention programs, and financial incentives, we have surpassed our goals in three of the major modifiable risk categories - smoking, blood pressure and cholesterol." Goodrich continued, "We've seen a 66 percent drop in tobacco use over time, for example, and reported a rate of smoking at 4 percent for 2007 compared with a national target of 12 percent by 2010."[71]

And for businesses, the benefits extend beyond the concrete savings in health care costs and the moral gratification of developing healthier workers. A 2007 nationwide survey of 355 human resources and health benefits managers suggested a strong correlation between wellness programs and increased productivity and market and shareholder value.[72] The Workplace Wellness Alliance (USWWA), an advocacy group promoting employer-based wellness programs, found an average 27 percent reduction in sick leave absenteeism and an average 32 percent reduction in worker's compensation costs.[73] The Business Roundtable, an association of CEO's from U.S. companies that employ over ten million workers, supported a study from Hewitt Associates that concluded, "large employers have come to believe that targeted improvements in wellness and prevention can improve health outcomes and reduce the costs of chronic illness, improving not only the company's cost profile, but also the productivity of their workforce."[74]

According to data from insurer Blue Cross, chronic diseases lead to an estimated 45 million sick days and $7.4 billion in lost productivity each year.[75] In the initial cost discussion, the negative impact of the cost of employer-sponsored health insurance on the ability of U.S. business to compete in the world was covered. Imagine the productivity changes and the subsequent value for these companies that would come out of decreasing the amount of sick days and increasing productivity. These studies demonstrate its feasibility simply through diminishing moral hazard and aligning the proper incentives to promote healthy behavior. This alteration in health care policy could spearhead a boon for U.S. industry.

Arguments have been made against the idea of incentive programs. Karen Davenport, the director of health policy at the Center for American Progress, states that incentives may "undermine one of the fundamental goals of health reform — ensuring that individuals with chronic illnesses and other health conditions do not pay more for health insurance and health care simply because they are sick."[76] First, I thought that the point of health reform was to develop a health care system that was more efficient, less expensive, with increased access and quality. I thought the goal of health reform was to transform our society into one that was healthier. I did not realize that a fundamental goal was equalizing the cost distribution among all citizens. Second, plenty of data has thus far been put forth that elucidates the perverse incentives and moral hazard that arise when this ideological approach expressed by Ms. Davenport is implemented in health care. This once again is viewing health care reform through the prism of the symptom rather than searching for the disease. This would be no different than a physician treating a young man with excessive thirst and frequent, large volume urination—classic symptoms of new-onset diabetes—with water restriction as opposed to insulin. Yet this refrain continues to resound and creates that noise that distorts true attempts at problem solving.

Ms. Davenport goes on to say, "Incentive plans that provide a 'bonus' to participating employees, or employees who reach specific health improvement milestones, can also be seen as a penalty for those employees who do not or cannot comply with the program." So are we to throw out a successful approach that turns the focus toward health and away from illness management? Are we to ignore the idea that the best way to minimize the need for health care is to promote healthy living? This again harkens to the acceptance of the prevalence of illness in our society, a sort of defeatist attitude as seen in those arguments against the potential positive effect of moral hazard and the value of cost sharing.

We need to begin to attack the very behaviors that lead to chronic illnesses. We need to begin to create a culture of health. Dismissing the potential gains for a large segment of the population out of concern for employees who do not comply with a health incentive program is illogical and poorly conceived. And incentives can be arranged so that those born with the misfortune of a genetic predisposition to an illness can win as well—diabetics can be incented to control their blood sugar levels to maintain them within an appropriate range, people with hypertension or elevated cholesterol can been rewarded for taking their medications or losing weight. If an employee is otherwise unwilling to participate in or comply with a health program, well that is a personal choice, but the negative consequences of that decision should fall squarely upon that person. As Ms. Davenport states, "These employees will pay more for their health insurance or for health services than their co-workers — colleagues who may do the exact same job but who, in effect, receive better total compensation."

That is exactly the point of patient incentives.

Provider Incentives

Incentives are a two way street. Improper economic incentives can promote physicians to over utilize health care similar to the way misaligned incentives compel patients to do the same. For the providers, this perversion revolves around financial reward. Physicians should order tests, perform procedures or set patient appointments based solely on medical necessity, not their bottom line. Unfortunately, in medicine like all other professions, there are those who focus primarily upon themselves, eschewing the good of others and the ethics of their profession for personal gain. They see illness as opportunity and a patient as a check book.

While this subgroup will always exist, they are the minority. No matter what system is established, they will always find ways to exploit that system for selfish ambition. However, they are not the sole force behind the provider-driven escalation in health care costs. It is the seduction of financial earnings that can ever so slightly alter the practice of medicine, even by those who maintain their patient's interests above their own. These are the physicians who can be positively influenced.

The goal of payment reform is to promote efficiency in diagnosis and treatment and to reward quality over quantity. But will payment reform truly place the patient at the center of the health care model? Will it sufficiently alter these subtle financial incentives and create a true alignment of incentives between patients and providers? The transformation of the health care system must encompass all aspects within the currently arranged structure that negatively impact the patient-provider relationship in order to reach its maximal effect, not focus on individual components.

To expand on this point, I am going develop an analogy that relates correcting the structural issue in our system to properly managing diabetes. As was noted previously, reforming cost sharing (minimizing moral hazard) places patients in the center of health care. This is the insulin for diabetes. The data has demonstrated the positive impact that comes from applying increased cost sharing to health care costs and the upward bending cost curve. But the treatment for a diabetic does not stop with medication. Doing such a thing would miss other opportunities to further impact the disease. Those other opportunities include weight loss, exercise and following a proper diet. Without applying these adjunctive steps, the diabetes will never fully be controlled. Incentives heighten the impact of the positive effect of removing moral hazard in much the same way. Patient incentives have already been covered, and their value in decreasing costs and increasing health is undeniable. Provider incentives will be impacted simply through minimizing the cost shielding that occurs from separating the patient's payment from the providers' charges. Simply put, it is more difficult to direct a patient to over utilize health care when you know that the patient carries the cost directly as opposed to passing a majority of the expenses through a third party payer. That subtle financial perversion for those honest providers becomes much less subtle. However, additional steps can be taken to further promote proper physician incentives through payment reform to continue to strengthen our new framework.

The most common reimbursement method in use is fee-for-service. In this model, each service carries its own charge and is paid separately. For example, the total charge to visit the family physician consists of the individual fees that include seeing the doctor, drawing blood, obtaining an EKG, having a chest x-ray, and so on. And when the radiologist reads the chest x-ray and the lab runs the blood, they too charge for their work. The concern that arises from this system is fairly obvious—providers get paid to do more. In addition, providers receive better pay to render services that carry a larger profit margin. This payment model within the currently arranged health care system can promote overutilization and increase expenditures.

Interestingly, this economic model where each item is purchased individually is the basis for the majority of transactions within society. We pay for each separate item or service at the grocery store, at the department store and at the mechanic's shop. Yet in these instances, we carry little concern regarding the overutilization of goods or services. What makes medicine so different? While this question will draw a multitude of responses, I will keep the spectrum narrowed for this discussion.

One part of the answer is that medicine is a unique service—the knowledge disproportionately rests with the provider. While I know little about engines, I can generally sniff out a mechanic running up unnecessary charges. This is much more difficult in medicine. But the second point that often gets pushed aside in the debate is that I care about the mechanic's service recommendations and their associated costs because I have to pay the charges personally. There is no middle man, no buffer. This is once again that ongoing theme of the moral hazard associated with paying 12 cents on the dollar for health care. If I had to pay only a small portion of the bill, then I would be less inclined to ensure I get sufficient value for my dollar. As a last point, in the other service-oriented industries transparency and competition protects the consumer and acts as a natural constraint on the system. Consumers can use the knowledge associated with transparent pricing and the effect of competition to their advantage. This aspect of normal market forces is absent in medicine. This is the extended view of health care consumerism that drives to create a culture of health, but the extent of that topic falls beyond the scope of this writing. I will further discuss alignment of incentives within the structure of the health care system as a whole after briefly touching on alternate payment models.

Capitation, a second payment model, is based upon the provider receiving a lump sum of money from an insuring entity to cover the costs of managing every aspect of health care for a beneficiary for a year. This approach leads to concern about promoting provider underutilization. If the cost of delivering patient care is nearing the total allotted amount for that patient, then the provider is left with the decision to either reduce potentially necessary services or take a financial loss. This leads to a shift in incentives to the other end of the spectrum and creates its own set of problems. As a result, capitation carries little favor among providers or patients and has become less utilized within the health care industry.

A more recently developed model combines a bit of both fee-for-service and capitation and has been called a bundled payment system, case rate payment or episode-based payment. In this approach, a single payment contracted in advance of the treatment covers all providers, procedures and any other items associated with a distinct episode of care. The reimbursement is based upon a calculation of the average cost to provide such a service. For example, if a patient is scheduled to undergo a cardiac bypass, then all services and providers involved in that case from the pre-operative coordinators, the cardiac surgeon, the hospital, physician consultants, home health care and follow-up visits are included in the payment. Efficient providers would return a profit while those that are less efficient would have to either improve or stop providing that service. This approach encourages coordination of care since any physician associated with the service is paid only if the cost of care is less than the reimbursed amount.

This approach to payment reform was evaluated when the Health Care Financing Administration (today's Centers for Medicare and Medicaid Services, CMS) developed a Medicare demonstration project of payment bundling to cover all of the inpatient and outpatient expenses associated with cardiac bypass surgery at four institutions in Boston, Atlanta, Ann Arbor, and Columbus, Ohio beginning in 1991.[77] During the first two years, Medicare and its beneficiaries saved more than $17 million on bypass surgery for an average savings of $4,700 per case. For three of four participating medical centers, the cost per bypass case actually fell during the first three years while other non-participating hospitals' costs increased. Despite accepting a decrease in reimbursement rates of at least 10 percent, the two non-academic centers experienced higher profits as a result of these improvements in cost containment. On the other hand, the two academic centers that accepted discounts of greater than 20 percent saw their average margins fall. One center achieved absolute cost reductions of just 4-6 percent, an insufficient improvement to cover the diminished reimbursement. The other academic failed to reduce costs, and its average profit margin went from approximately $3,000 to a loss of $4,000 to $6,000. Importantly, evaluation of this demonstration project found no decrease in the quality of care delivered.

The Geisinger Health System recently implemented this approach in their cardiac bypass program. When the difference in expenditures between a group prior to the alteration in payment approach was compared to a group after the change, hospital costs dropped by 5 percent, again demonstrating the ability of medical institutions to increase efficiency.[78] This model continues to show promise and additional testing is ongoing in other areas such as knee replacement surgery.

Payment bundling is therefore a potential opportunity to impact one aspect of the structural problem within our system, but payment modification alone does not correct the totality of the structural issue to gain maximal benefit from reform. It is a potential piece of the puzzle, but it does not align patient and provider incentives, nor does it impact moral hazard.

Other alternative payment approaches range from a physician employment model, where physicians receive a set salary irrespective of the volume of services, to accountable care organizations (ACOs), where health care providers are incentivized to band together to provide greater coordination of care. The employee model is utilized at the Mayo Clinic to great effect, but its application outside of the unique environment of academic centers is debatable. ACOs are currently being evaluated in Medicare pilot projects, and some communities are implementing this approach outside of government involvement. Payment reform systems are also looking into pay-for-performance models that tie reimbursement to performance with the goal of delivering financial rewards to promote utilization of more cost effective, successful treatments.

Data regarding the effectiveness of these alternative reimbursement models is generally scarce. To that end, multiple demonstration projects have been proposed in the Patient Protection and Affordable Care Act (PPACA), and previous Medicare initiatives have also begun to look into their ability to control costs. Time will tell whether future efficiencies can arise from altered payment approaches, but as was seen in the bundling payment approach, the potential exists.

That being said, I have one point to make, and it harkens back to incentives being a two way street. These experimental models to find the most cost effective reimbursement arrangement are couched within an inefficient health care delivery system and only look at a small portion of the picture. And while these models, unlike the PPACA (to be discussed later), do at least begin to work on one structural problem, they still are a top down, centralized approach to health care reform. The perverse incentive of financial gain is still in place for the provider, and in the structure of the traditional insurance model, the patient remains insulated from the cost and thus subtly removed from the totality of the decision-making process.

The value associated with the physician and patient having the discussion regarding the pros and cons of a procedure within the context of cost is still not achieved. While payment reform may appropriately decrease costs as noted in Geisinger Health Center's cardiac program, a physician may then be less apt to discuss alternate treatment options that return less in payment but perhaps best fit the patient's desire of less morbidity or risk. The cost to the system and society has taken precedent over the patient who is still not at the center of the health care model. The insurance company sets the reimbursement, and the physician tries to squeeze the treatment options into that cost structure. Since the patient is still not in control of the payment, the incentives for both the physician and patient are not optimally aligned. The patient needs to be the primary influencer of treatment in a model based on transparency of cost and outcome associated with each available option.

For a recent example to elucidate this point: A patient came to see me because she was in the process of passing a kidney stone. I ran through the normal list of treatment options ranging from waiting to see if she could pass the stone; performing shock wave lithotripsy (ESWL) where a machine is placed on the abdomen and high energy sound waves are passed through the body to fragment the stone; or passing a camera into the urinary system and breaking the stone under direct vision using a laser (ureteroscopy). Each of these options has their set of risks and benefits. Doing nothing obviously costs nothing to the medical system. ESWL is more costly and slightly less effective than ureteroscopy, but ESWL is also less invasive and carries less risk. She informed me that she had a high deductible health plan with a health savings account and she had not met her deductible. We then had a frank discussion on cost in the context of the risks and benefits associated with each treatment option. She chose the more successful but more invasive ureteroscopy. She was directly involved in the decision making process. She could have opted to undergo the more costly but less effective ESWL if she were risk averse, but the point is, it was her choice.

But if this example is approached from a centrally managed health care system with minimal cost sharing where reimbursement for a medical problem is forced into the set framework of a bundled payment, then the patient is again kept on the outside of the process. The incentives of each party involved are still are not completely aligned. If the episode of "kidney stone" pays a set amount, then the incentive from the physician is still influenced by economics and this still subtly impacts the direction of the treatment discussion. A physician would be more likely to direct a patient toward the procedure that carries the greatest profit margin. While the overall approach may cut costs for the health care system and society as a whole, the patient is still not the true focus of the model. Instead of allowing the patient to make a decision based on their personal desires, the choice will move to the physician who is now incented to perform the least costly procedure in order to maximize profit for that episode of care. The patient who may have been willing to pay more for less risk with the understanding of decreased efficacy may be persuaded to follow the procedure that produces greater profit for the physician.

I am going to extend this and place hypothetical numbers into the mix. Let's say ureteroscopy costs $2,500 and has a success rate of 96 percent, but a camera is placed inside the body to resolve the medical issue. The ESWL costs $3,000 with an 85 percent success rate but is less invasive. We'll put the bundled payment at $3,500. In the system where the patient is insulated from the cost as a result of minimal cost sharing, the physician sees a larger margin and higher likelihood of success with the more aggressive ureteroscopy. In this scenario, the patient is left on the periphery of the true decision. The subtle effect of financial gain for the provider is still at play. In the alternate approach as noted above where my patient carried personal financial stake in the surgery, she was presented each option with their associated risks, benefits, and cost, and she was directly involved in the decision-making process. I have had a few patients participating in consumer-driven health plans, and they have made different decisions on care, but in each instance, the patient was able to choose treatment based on that which was most important to them.

Health care reform must be based upon the more natural realignment of incentives that occurs when the patient becomes the center of the health care system. And this can only truly happen when patients become more intricately involved in the costs of their care through greater cost sharing and transparency. As was noted through the prior discussion on cost sharing, costs do come down in this model, but it is accomplished at the patient and physician level, not at the bureaucratic or insurance industry level. Payment reform can follow the transformation of the health care system, but focusing on reforming the payment system within a broken health care system will not lead to the greatest possible benefit.

The value for our society that can come from choosing the proper structure upon which to build the next health care system will only be fully realized if we honestly evaluate the shortcomings in our current system. We must search out and eliminate the underlying processes that pervert healthy lifestyle choices and create a system that maximizes the incentives that promote a culture of health in our society. The evidence, based on studies and data as opposed to ideology or politics, has defined the alterations that can act as a framework for an efficient, cost effective 21st century health care model. The structure must be patient-centered with the proper alignment of incentive for all participants in the system.

Massachusetts versus Indiana: From Hypothetical to Reality

The data covered thus far has hopefully brought greater understanding of the potential effects associated with instituting different health care reform ideas. However, there is nothing like the value of seeing these policies as they play out in the real world. This frees us to move beyond the hypothetical nature of studies and evaluate these models in action.

Fortunately, we in the U.S. have been given the wonderful gift of federalism that allows us to determine the impact of changes set in motion at the state level before releasing them on the nation. We can "experiment" with differing approaches to health care reform in the states, using them as a Petri dish for reform ideas, if you will. Again harkening back to the practice of medicine, this would be comparable to running a medical trial and then applying that evidence to direct the appropriate treatment choice to cure a disease process. This is the crux of the practice of medicine in today's society: an evidence-based approach to disease management.

Would it not be inane to ignore this information when it comes to choosing the proper direction of health care reform? We cannot ignore such vital data and expect to successfully transform our health care system. We continually need to keep the goal of our task in the forefront, and any information that can directly bring real life models into the evaluation process carries so much value. Tossing aside this information is nothing more than succumbing to the noise of ideology or politics.

Two state models have been chosen based upon their divergent approaches to correcting their local health care issues. The approaches can be broken down into two overarching themes, the two alternate philosophies toward the reform process. The one approach utilized to craft the Patient Protection and Affordable Care Act focuses on a centrally-driven reform model, one that builds upon traditional comprehensive insurance while further augmenting government intervention in the health care system. The second approach is based upon empowering individuals instead of the government by providing information and promoting personal financial responsibility to support a position of ownership in health care decisions. [79]

In the first approach, the structure of our current employer-sponsored third-party payer system remains intact and is managed through increased regulatory oversight and further expansion of government into the realm of insurance. The underlying goal is dispersion of risk among the population as a whole while simultaneously insulating the individual from the direct cost of health care. Maximal health coverage is obtained in advance of illness and since insurance covers a greater portion of medical costs via decreased cost sharing, the individual financial risk is minimized. The money within this system is not exchanged between the patient and physician, the two parties directly involved in the transaction of the health care service, but is instead managed by a third party. As such, patients are removed from the costs of both purchasing insurance and the utilization of health services. However, despite being detached from the costs directly, individuals do still pay for this system. They just have little control over their personal health care dollars. Cost containment is borne more out of market manipulation and bureaucratic management than changes at the individual level. The supporters of this ideal follow a belief in the social redistributive element of insurance, a health care safety net directed by intellectual leaders in our government who are more able to intercede and control costs than the ordinary citizens and other participants in the health care market.

The second contrary approach is grounded in free market ideals and is often referred to as health care consumerism. This has been discussed previously under **Cost Sharing**. In this model, individuals or their employers purchase high deductible health plans to cover either catastrophic costs or the other more costly aspects of health care. As a way to help defray the impact of the higher deductibles, the plans are associated with a medical savings account such as a health saving account (HSA). The idea is to place the patient at the center of health care decision-making, empowering individuals to control more of their personal health care dollars while providing for catastrophic coverage. Instead of insulating the patient and removing them from the financial impact of health care expenditures, they become integrated directly into the system. It is a "skin in the game" approach. The goal is to encourage personal responsibility for managing lifestyle choices as well as health care purchasing behaviors. It is about supplying greater health information and support tools, increasing transparency of price and quality, diminishing the impact of moral hazard and properly realigning incentives to encourage personal involvement in all aspects of one's health. The expectation is that through rewarding participation in health programs (e.g. weight loss, exercise, diabetes management) and maintenance of health characteristics (proper body mass index, smoking avoidance, cholesterol control), a culture of health arises.[79]

This approach believes that patients can become more intelligent consumers and can learn to better manage their health; that individuals are truly able to make smart decisions for themselves and are not dependent upon the government to make those decisions for them. And when the culture of health becomes properly incented, health increases, the demand for health care decreases and costs go down. When health care is needed, the consumer is more apt to tightly manage their expenses and expect value for their dollars, for as the saying goes, no one spends other people's money as carefully as their own.

The Massachusetts Model

I am going to first discuss the Massachusetts health care system as a surrogate for the Patient Protection and Affordable Care Act (PPACA). This system is a model for reform among those who believe in a government-regulated system. As such, studying the effects of this model gives us great insight into the expected impact of implementing this approach to health care reform at the national level.

In 2006 the state of Massachusetts passed a sweeping overhaul of its health care system. This piece of state legislation acted as a template for the development of the current health care law, and its component parts are essentially the building blocks for the PPACA. The Massachusetts' reform included an individual and employer mandate; established the

Commonwealth Connector, an insurance exchange; developed a new program called Commonwealth Care to deliver health insurance subsidies for families with incomes up to 300 percent of the federal poverty level ($66,000 for a family of four); expanded the Medicaid program to 100 percent of the federal poverty level; and broadened the state government's control over the health care system.

While the primary objective of the program was to expand coverage to all of the residents of Massachusetts, the expectation of cost savings were trumpeted as well. After signing the measure, Gov. Mitt Romney wrote, "Every uninsured citizen in Massachusetts will soon have affordable health insurance and the costs of health care will be reduced." Suffice to say, if a comparison between the Massachusetts model and the PPACA had to be relayed in medical terms, I would describe the PPACA as the Massachusetts reform on steroids. The Medicaid expansion and exchange subsidies in the PPACA extend well beyond the levels in Massachusetts. So did this reform cure the ills of health care in Massachusetts? Is this an effective approach to reforming our national health care system?

Health insurance coverage has increased, and the state now boasts an uninsured rate of 2.7 percent. Prior to the institution of reform, Massachusetts had one of the lowest rates of uninsured in the nation, estimated at 8.5 to 10 percent (compared to 15 percent nationally). While the estimates of the uninsured rise to 5.4 percent when the Census Bureau data gathered from door to door surveys is used as opposed to the phone surveys that lead to the oft quoted 2.7 percent rate, coverage has indeed expanded. The program has been a success in that regard.

But is this broadening of insurance coverage sustainable and what has been the impact associated with the alteration in the health care delivery system? The goal of any reform is to bring greater access to health care for all individuals, but if the plan is not built upon a financial model grounded in economic reality, then it will fail and our objective will not be met, no matter how sincere or benevolent that original goal might have been. So what did we find in this model, this surrogate for our national plan? Is this a potential solution to our health care woes?

"The state's individuals, families, and employers, as well as state and local government, are all struggling under the weight of high and rapidly

rising health care costs, which is creating barriers to accessing care, cutting into wage growth, stifling job creation, and preempting spending in other sectors of the economy.[80]

Unfortunately, this is not a resounding statement of success or sustainability. The author: the Massachusetts Division of Healthcare Finances and Policy (DHCFP), the group that manages the health care program for the state. The timing: the April 2010 final report. The cost crisis has reached this level of economic woe despite the fact that the reform program is barely three years into its existence.

The report goes on to say that "spending on health care is 15 percent higher than the rest of the nation, even when accounting for higher wages in Massachusetts and spending on medical research and education." This excess level of spending exceeds the percentage noted prior to full implementation of the plan. In 2007, health care expenditures were expected to account for 15.2 percent of GDP in Massachusetts compared to 13.7 percent for the nation, a difference of 11 percent. That gap has now widened to 15 percent.

Unfortunately, in either a complete lack of awareness or blind political ideology, the directors of DHCFP, those proponents of this system, go on to say that the cost increases impacting their state, those increases that are worsening and are greatly exceeding the rest of the nation where this legislation has not been enacted, are not a result of the Massachusetts' reform. I find this level of arrogance or ignorance an unbelievable and unfortunate condition that commonly affects either ideologues or the self-serving. If the effort to create an apples-to-apples comparison has been made, then how can the directors so blatantly disregard the direct findings of their own evaluation? This lack of insight is disturbing. Beyond this self-evaluation of the system, other reviews of the Massachusetts model have come to similar conclusions.

The rate of health care spending in Massachusetts has increased 7.5 percent per year from 2006 through 2008, which is higher than the 6.1 percent growth rate in national health care expenditures over that same period.[81] To draw on additional data to once again add perspective to these numbers, the Massachusetts' Executive Office of Health and Human Services on February 6, 2008 evaluated the state's health care cost trends from 1991 to 2005. They concluded, "Though we start from a higher base, Massachusetts health care spending and health insurance premiums are growing at a similar rate as nationally." So not only is there a gap in spending between Massachusetts and the U.S, but the growth rate in spending has moved from a trend similar to the U.S. to one that exceeds it by 23 percent annually (7.5 percent divided by 6.1 percent). This is the worst of all possibilities: the health care costs are higher and the cost curve is bending upward more quickly.

To employ another saying in medicine: "When a (patient) problem arises, look first at where we (doctors) have tread", meaning problems that crop up after an intervention are more apt to be a direct result of that intervention. When a patient sees me after a medication change or a surgery and things are not going well, I have to look in the mirror and accept that my treatment is not working. It is not rocket science; it is accountability. The intervention prior to the rapid escalation in health care costs for residents of Massachusetts was the adoption of the reform plan.

Further evaluation leads to similar conclusions. According to an analysis by the RAND Corporation, "in the absence of policy change, health care spending in Massachusetts is projected to nearly double to $123 billion in 2020, increasing 8 percent faster than the state's gross domestic product."[82]

Unfortunately, these cost increases are not restricted to the public domain. Despite supporters of the program previously suggesting that reform would reduce the price of insurance policies by 25-40 percent, private health insurance premiums have risen instead, growing at a 9 percent annual rate compared to 6.7 percent nationally.[83,84,85] A recent report from Stanford University found that since the reform passed, private employer-sponsored premiums for individuals increased 6 percent more in Massachusetts compared to the rest of the nation, and this problem was even worse in the small-group market where insurance costs grew by 14 percent.[86] While the difference in the rate of change in premiums varies between the two reports, the trends consistently show costs rising more steeply than the U.S. where this plan has not been enacted. These findings in the trend levels for premiums were also echoed in a report prepared in February 2010 for that same Massachusetts Executive

Office of Health and Human Services. This report confirmed the above mentioned findings when it stated, "Massachusetts has higher health insurance premiums than the U.S. average, and for at least the past five years premiums have grown at a faster rate."[87]

According to an article in the Boston Globe in July 2010, the escalation in premiums has created a recent rise in small companies dropping coverage for their workers and encouraging them to sign up for the state-subsidized plan, a move that will further exacerbate the cost issue for the state (this is anecdotal based on recent statements from small businesses and insurance brokers and has yet to show up in the data). This will also cost these companies a fee, since an employer mandate is in force for the state as part of the reform package. Since 70 percent of new jobs come from small business, is there any wonder why job creation is being stifled as employers struggle with ballooning premiums that will soon be followed by the useless loss of revenue for mandate penalties?

And these problems persist despite the state dropping coverage for 30,000 legal immigrants, delaying benefits for up to 18,000 residents who qualify for fully funded health care and eliminating dental coverage for 92,000 low-income enrollees.[88,89] In order to add more revenue, the legislators increased the cigarette tax $1 a pack (generally a tax on the poor) and initiated $89 million in new fees on the health care industry, all while receiving $1.5 billion from the U.S. government (which begs the question: if this plan is released nationally, who picks up the excess tab when the bill is greater than we can afford?).

The effects of this reform process extend beyond the issue of rising costs. The average wait time to see a primary care physician in Boston in 2007 was 34 days—now it is 63 days.[90] In a May 2010 report, the Urban Institute found that almost one-third (32.8%) of Massachusetts residents with full-year insurance coverage reported some type of problem getting health care in the past 12 months. This included more than one in five (22.5%) who reported problems getting care related to access to providers, and almost one in five (18.1%) who reported that they were not able to get the health care that they needed because of cost.[91]

In 2009, only 44 percent of internal medicine practices were accepting new patients, down from 66 percent in 2005. The proportion of family medicine physician offices accepting new patients declined from 70 percent in 2007 to 60 percent in 2009, and only 38 percent of internal medicine and family medicine/general practice physician offices, those gate keepers of medicine, reported that they accept insurance products from the Commonwealth Connector (the subsidized insurance exchange program).[92]

If we actually pause and take an honest look at the data, a definitive pattern has formed...costs have skyrocketed and access has decreased (remember that having an insurance card does not equate to having access to health care). Is quality, the third pillar of health care reform, at risk as well?

As a result of the concerns that health care spending will overwhelm the state's budget, Governor Deval Patrick in February 2010 opened the possibility of capping the fees physicians, hospitals, medical imaging centers and other health care services can charge as a way to constrain the rapidly rising costs. This equates to price controls, and this approach comes with its own expense. Physicians will flee the state, further exacerbating the access problem, and quality will be negatively impacted as well.

In the 1970s and 80s, 30 states instituted a similar policy of price controls by capping fees that hospitals could charge. A study in the New England Journal of Medicine in 1988 looked at the mortality rates in those states and compared them to mortality rates in other states without the capped fees. The study concluded that those states with the capped fees had a 5-6 percent higher death rate among a comparable cohort of patients than those hospitals without the caps. Is this next pillar to fall in Massachusetts reform? This runs contrary the Hippocratic Oath, and any reform process for our health care system must first follow that same hallowed principle of medical practice.

So the positive outcome from the Massachusetts model is increased health insurance coverage. Sounds great, but access to care, the real point of insurance, has decreased. And costs have dramatically increased. And soon, quality will decrease as the death rate rises under price controls or other rationing methods. No data has yet to demonstrate short-term, much less long-term, sustainability of this model.

Those who run the system argue that the costs are within budgeted expectations. If that is the case, then after reading of the cost problems and their impact across all segments of the Massachusetts economy, I can only suggest that the people of Massachusetts take a better look at those who are writing their budget. They obviously have a very different definition of budget than the rest of us who have to live in the reality of the economics of this world.

The structural issues of the health care system were not addressed but instead exacerbated under this system. Instead of diverting a bus heading for a cliff, this approach applied greater pressure to the accelerator. I will leave the Massachusetts discussion with one final commentary, and one that I think is the most insightful and meaningful, and one that succinctly confirms the data presented above. This is from March 16, 2010 and comes from current Massachusetts state treasurer Timothy P. Cahill, a former Democrat who is running as an independent for governor.[93]

The local plan enacted in 2006 has succeeded only because of huge subsidies and favorable regulatory changes from the federal government. And he (Cahill) said that while the Massachusetts program has increased access to health insurance, it has nothing to rein in underlying cost increases, meaning it is steering more people to a broken system.

"If President (Barack) Obama and the Democrats repeat the mistake of the health insurance reform adopted here in Massachusetts on a national level, they will threaten to wipe out the American economy within four years," the treasurer said.

This approach undertaken in Massachusetts appears to be an object lesson in how not to reform a health care system, yet the evidence was either ignored or perverted during the reform debates. This problem of cost containment (and access and quality) and sustainability associated with increasing government intervention in a health care system based upon the flawed structural concept of comprehensive health insurance is not specific to Massachusetts.

In 1994, Tennessee launched TennCare, a broad expansion of Medicaid. The program successfully cut the state's uninsured rate to about 6 percent. But in 2005, the Tennessee legislature approved Democrat

Governor Phil Bredesen's budget proposal, which included plans to cut 323,000 beneficiaries from TennCare. The program, despite a special arrangement that allowed the federal government to fund a majority of the cost, was described as a "budget buster" and threatened to drive the state into bankruptcy. In addition to decreasing the number of beneficiaries, benefits were reduced as well, including restrictions on prescription drug coverage. Tennessee discovered that cost sustainability is necessary to maintain a successful program, and the expansion of Medicaid does not achieve that end.

In 2003, Maine expanded its Medicaid program to cover 22 percent of the population while also creating a "public option" known as Dirigo-Choice to compete with private plans. The system that was supposed to save money has cost taxpayers $155 million and rising. The premiums for DirigoChoice have increased 74 percent, and few low-income Mainers have been able to afford the premiums, even at subsidized rates. The state legislature proposed an infusion of funds through a beer, wine and soda tax, but that was rejected by Maine voters 2:1. Last year the legislature passed a 2 percent tax on paid health insurance claims contrary to public wishes.

Since 1988, many other states—Oregon, Minnesota, Vermont, Washington—have enacted reforms aimed at achieving universal coverage. All offered new government subsidies and/or expanded Medicaid. All have failed. They were all built upon a broken structure, doing nothing but exacerbating the underlying flaws within the system. Just like Massachusetts, they focused on peripheral problems without understanding the underlying flaws within the structure of the system. To quote a group of physicians from Harvard who happens to favor a single payer system, "There is little reason to think that the current Massachusetts reform, or a national plan modeled on these state reforms, would have any better long-term success." [9.]

I could not agree more with their assessment of this approach, for they realize that repeating failed policies will not work. We as a society must heed the data, define the true issues and honestly search out real solutions. If we continue to be swayed by those who create so much noise, who distract and detract from truthful evaluation of the problems and solutions, then we too will be destined for the same predictable collapse. The evidence provides a very clear picture.

The Indiana Experiment

Just as the Massachusetts reform can be used as a proxy for the PPACA, the Indiana approach can act as a surrogate for the patient-centered reform model known as health care consumerism. The data regarding cost savings, decreasing the rate of rise in health care spending, and the improvement on the level of health associated with this approach is clear from the previous studies. Once again though, this comparison is undertaken to evaluate the effects of the plan when implemented in a real world setting, allowing the discussion to move from the hypothetical to reality.

The data will differ somewhat from Massachusetts in that the Indiana plan was implemented for state employees only, not all state residents. With this being the case, it is not possible to track the direct impact of this model on the expansion of health insurance. However, state expenditures, health care utilization, trends in health status, and the financial impact on the state employees participating in the program can be extracted. The cost outcomes can then be utilized to project the sustainability of this model as well as its ability to potentially impact issues such as expanding access to health care.

The Indiana approach has been less scrutinized than Massachusetts, and as a result, less comparative data is available. Mercer—a large consulting firm that among other things specializes in assessing outcomes of the application of different health care models (not a politicized think tank or ideological group)—was requested to dispatch their actuaries to evaluate the impact of the Indiana health care consumerism plan. Most of the following information was gleaned from their report released on May 20, 2010 called Consumer-Driven Health Plan Case Study: State of Indiana. I do not have the hard data and am dependent upon Mercer's accurate and honest evaluation.

Indiana, like most states, was struggling with the rising cost of health care for its 30,000 state employees. And in a similar fashion to our country, the costs were following that upward bending curve and were negatively impacting the budget. The health insurance plans at the time were generous and had limited cost sharing, factors that insulated the employees from the cost of their care. In 2006, the first CDHP with a Health Savings Account (HSA) was offered as a new concept. The following year, a second CDHP plan was introduced. At the same time, the initial four comprehensive health plans were consolidated into two plans, an HMO and a PPO. Data from the HMO is not available since the plan is closing at the end of 2010.

Without getting too bogged down into all of the plans' specifics, their general structure needs to be briefly covered to allow a more complete understanding of the data. CDHP1, the first consumerism plan, carries the greatest cost sharing. It is based upon the annual maximum allowable deductible and maximum out of pocket expenditures as permitted by federal law. The employee pays nothing toward the premium, the state covers 55 percent of the deductible by placing funds directly into the employee's personal HSA, and the employee can contribute pre-tax dollars into the HSA up to the maximum amount, again as determined by federal law. The employee then must pay for all medical care using either the HSA or their personal funds until the deductible is met. At that point, the employee is responsible for 20 percent of additional medical costs until reaching the out of pocket maximum, at which point the insurance covers the remaining charges.

CDHP2 has less cost sharing but follows a similar approach. The deductible and maximum out-of-pocket expenditures are less, and the employee has to contribute a small amount toward the premium. The state pays 27 percent into the HSA, and the remaining portion of the plan is similar to CDHP1. In both of the CDHP plans, any money remaining in the HSA belongs to the employee and accumulates over time.

The PPO and HMO plans are similar to the comprehensive plans that most in the U.S. use now. These plans have less cost sharing, lower deductibles (zero for the HMO), lower out of pocket maximums, and no HSAs. The employee pays more toward the premiums compared to the CDHP plans, and since the cost sharing is minimized and no HSAs are allowed, the employee is shielded from the losses or gains of over or underutilization of health services.

Preventive services are covered at 100 percent and a financial incentive to avoid tobacco use is common to all plans. Now that the plan structure has been laid out, the impact needs to be examined.

In the first year of the new plan, only 1,400 employees enrolled in CDHP1. This grew to 6,300 after the addition of CDHP2 the following year and has rapidly grown to 12,100 in 2008 and 15,500 (49 percent of all employees) in 2009. The enrollment in the two CDHPs has reached 70 percent of all employees for calendar year 2010, a growth of 1,500 percent since their inception. This rapid growth is telling—if the state employees were unhappy with the CDHP plans, word would spread and enrollment would fall, not increase. The obvious assumption based on the growth would thus be that the employees were actually quite fond of the plan and felt that these consumerism plans offered more value to them personally. This assumption is further validated by the fact that only 3 percent of employees moved in the opposite direction from a CDHP back to a comprehensive plan.

Cost containment was the initial objective of these plans, so did they work? Mercer found an average annual savings for the state of 12.5 percent for CDHP1 and 7.6 percent for CDHP2 for an overall savings of 10.7 percent. The total average annual state claims cost (plus HSA value for consumerism plans) for the PPO, CDHP2 and CDHP1 plans were $12,317, $9,444 and $5,462, respectively. With enrollment at 70 percent for 2010, the state is expected to save $17 to $23 million this year alone. To add emphasis in case that point was missed—COST SAVINGS of almost 11 PERCENT! Sorry about the yelling, but sometimes it is necessary. Indiana's assistant general counsel Anita Samuel noted, "The state has estimated savings of $42 million since introducing innovative consumer-driven plans to state employees."[95]

As Mercer points out, the potential of consumer-driven health plans to be part of a reform proposal to achieve that critical need (for Indiana and the U.S.) of decreasing cost and bending the cost curve downward was validated within the Indiana approach.

The necessary follow-up question: Did the savings for the state occur at the expense of the employees who had to pick up more of the cost? Applying a little common sense, one would doubt so many employees would flock to the CDHPs if they were personally paying more, and the facts support this supposition. State employees enrolled in the CDHPs are expected to have collectively deposited $7 to $8 million in their personal savings accounts in 2010 alone, meaning that they are in essence getting a raise in their take-home pay at a time when those not in this plan are seeing a stagnation of their salary. As of September 30, 2009, state employees had a total HSA balance of $28.1 million, savings that are growing and can be utilized to protect against future health care expenses. This is money that employees are keeping for themselves, money that would have otherwise been lost to the insurance industry. And since this money is growing tax-free, employees have been taking advantage and partially funding their HSAs as a method of saving for the future.

So how did these cost savings come about? The data from Indiana demonstrated a decrease in health care utilization rates that mirrored the cost sharing spectrum, similar to the finding in the RAND Health Insurance Experiment. Utilization was the highest in the minimal cost sharing PPO plan and the least in CDHP1, a trend that persisted even as more and more employees flocked from the PPO to the consumer-driven plans. The participants in the consumerism plans had less physician office visits, less hospital admissions, shorter length of hospital stays, and they were more likely to see their primary care doctor than a specialist. Those in CDHP1 visited the ER 47 percent less often and used generic medications 15 percent more frequently than those in the PPO plan.

Demographically, the CDHP participants had a lower average age but a higher average family size compared to the PPO members—a younger population will have lower costs than an older one but larger family size will lead to greater costs. In an attempt to ascertain the impact of the plan type on cost/utilization and create a more direct comparison, Mercer adjusted the differences in average annual claims cost based on plan design as well as health and demographic variations between the three plans. In doing so, they found that the participants in CDHP1 and CDHP2 saved $1,535 and $940, respectively, in relation to the PPO purely as a result of the positive effect of the consumerism plans. This confirms the impact of the cost sharing data from our previous studies.

Of course, health care systems are about more than just cost. One of the main concerns regarding these plans is their potential to cause participants to avoid necessary care. However, the question of avoidance of necessary care can be difficult to extract from data. It can take years to truly evaluate whether the reduction in utilization was a result of missing appropriate care versus avoiding unnecessary care versus decreased demand resulting from improved health status. However, one telling item was noted in the report. The state's health risk scores have slightly improved since the adoption of the CDHPs despite the aging of the covered population. And this occurred while utilization of health care services decreased. While the four year time frame since the health plans began is still fairly short, this finding certainly implies that the participants may actually be avoiding not only unnecessary care but are also becoming healthier. And just like utilization, the decrease in the risk scores correlated positively with increased cost sharing. The PPO risk score continued to increase the fastest and was followed by CDHP2 and then CDHP1.

While it is postulated that the sickest would likely linger in the more comprehensive PPO plan, this would mean that the new enrollees migrating into the consumerism plans from the PPO would be less healthy, and as the CDHP enrollment grows, the risk scores should rise substantially for these plans. In reality, CDHP1 risk scores have remained stable while CDHP2 only increased slowly. Risk scores are associated with health status, and this could therefore be interpreted that the health status of those more engaged in managing their health care dollars became more health conscious. Again, this same finding was noted in the Safeway and Johnson & Johnson data.

Now I would agree that some adverse selection is at play, and this is driving a portion of the rise in risk scores for the PPO plan, but the positive message from this data is that as these less healthy members move down the cost sharing scale, we do not see the expected concomitant worsening in health status in the consumerism groups. Are behavioral choices leading to better health? Some of that appears to be at play.

Mercer concluded that there was no evidence that participants in CDHPs were avoiding care, and that sources of savings appear to come from better use of health care resources and more cost conscious decision making. This matches with the goals as laid out by those in Indiana's state government. "Gov. Daniels introduced an innovative, consumer-driven health care option for state employees for plan year 2006," Samuel said. "The goal of the consumer-driven plan was to improve health outcomes and make more efficient use of health care dollars over the long term by empowering employees to keep themselves and their families healthy." The returns thus far appear to point to a mission accomplished.

While consumerism plans have not been enacted broadly enough in other states, large companies have recently been implementing them. I previously discussed Johnson & Johnson as well as Safeway, Inc. and its Healthy Measures program, a step to expand the positive impact of incentivization that has yet to be incorporated in Indiana beyond the prevention of tobacco use. This additional step could lead to even greater cost savings and improvement in employees' health. Please also read about Whole Foods Market, Inc., another example of real-life cost savings that are possible with well-designed, consumerism-based re-forms.

Massachusetts versus Indiana: Comparative Effectiveness Research

According to the Kaiser Family Foundation, "the aim of comparative effectiveness research (CER) is to improve health outcomes by develop-ing and disseminating evidence-based information to patients, providers, and health care decision-makers about the effectiveness of treatments relative to other options."[96] This approach was incorporated into the PPACA, and the creators of that legislation thought so highly of CER that they expanded funding and created a new institution to coordinate and support research activities. Those so focused on CER as a means to evaluate the efficacy and cost of comparable medical treatments seem to have missed its biggest and most important application: the development of an efficacious and efficient health care system. I think it is about time to apply this approach.

Before moving into the discussion, one point needs to be made: no health care system will likely ever be perfect. As with government systems, each have their pluses and minuses, and none fit all of the criteria that we as individuals and members of a society deem as ideal. But the goal is to find the one that works best, at least for now, at least until we come up with a better way to manage health.

We need to focus on making wise, well thought out decisions that are not based in ideology and the noise of politics, decisions that are not made in a harried or fragmented manner, decisions that do not bend to fit special interests or particular segments of society. And we definitely cannot transform our health care system into one that increases costs, decreases access or worsens quality. We need to remember that if we choose poorly, if we blindly follow the clamor of political beliefs, beliefs that should have nothing to do with curing the ills of our current health care system, we and the generations that follow will suffer. Too much is at stake to support or refute reform ideas because our political stripe directs us so.

One more point along a similar train of thought. I have read so much about the different approaches to reform. I have poured over arguments and studies that supposedly support or refute one side or the other. Some arguments are easily dissected, some are valid. But most seem to focus on minor aspects of the whole ideal. I covered this briefly in a prior discussion. For example, some argue against the value of health care consumerism and the tax deductibility of HSAs for those who pay no taxes. Instead of locking ourselves into current law, why not think creatively. Maybe we can simply alter the system to where the financial incentive is the same, whether the amount deposited comes from an individual making $30,000 or $300,000. Why throw out a potentially effective solution by viewing it through a narrowed lens of current law or thought?

The task is not to focus on the negative side of an effective instrument but to rather find a way to modify the instrument so that the negative aspect is blunted while the positive is enhanced. Is this not a better approach than utilizing a broken instrument that has been shown to fail and expecting it to solve the problem that it exacerbates? If I place a patient on chemotherapy for bladder cancer that causes severe nausea and the cancer continues to grow, I do not just treat the nausea and ignore the cancer's lack response to my management. I have merely palliated a poor treatment choice, and the disease persists and will worsen. On the other hand, if the cancer does respond to the chemotherapy, then modifying the negative consequences by correcting the nausea improves the ability of the effective treatment to be continued. We have found the proper cure, and we have now added strength to our regimen.

But we have a tendency to get so enthralled with our own arguments and have such a strong desire to be right, and as a result, potentially beneficial ideas are pigeon-holed, labeled and cast aside. We are in desperate need of truthful discussion and openness to ideas that may not fit our narrowed perspective. It is a grand task to perhaps alter the ideals that we hold as true, and while this may not be entirely possible, one thing that is without dispute: a plan without a basis in the reality of this world will unquestionably fail. A plan derived from ideology and not evidence will fail.

So what have we learned from the reality of the health care reform processes as implemented at the state level? What would comparative effectiveness research tell us about the different approaches to reform? It is really a rhetorical question, and hopefully not out of personal bias. The data from the evaluation of the impact of the reform plan instituted in Massachusetts is fairly obvious: it is neither a sustainable nor an effective approach to reform. It has expanded coverage, but as the costs continue to escalate, state assistance for coverage cannot be maintained. The economics of the state cannot support a reform that has done nothing but broaden an ineffective health care delivery structure.

Any attempt at cost control in the Massachusetts plan is picking at the edges. State officials have considered global payments to physicians, price controls in the form of caps on provider charges, reductions in amount insurers can charge for premiums, utilization of information technology, implementation of medical homes—some of these programs will defray costs, some will negatively impact quality and access to care, but none will cure the disease within the system. This is no different than giving nausea medication to our previous cancer patient on chemotherapy while ignoring the progressing disease.

In the attempt to reform the health care system in Massachusetts, the wrong treatment pathway was chosen. And none of these additional attempts to alter the progressively worsening crisis resolves the true fundamental flaws in the system—the perversion of moral hazard and lack of incentives associated with separating the participants from the costs of medical care. None truly promote personal responsibility for managing one's health—not just the short term impact of decreasing the utilization of health services, but the long term impact of healthy living that decreases self-inflicted disease. None place the provider in a position whereby upon receiving payment for a service delivered, that provider carries more direct financial accountability to the patient of delivering value for that service. None realign the incentives to promote healthy lifestyle choices. In actuality, these ideas run contrary to our current system and the Massachusetts model whereby the cost is covered by some nameless third party institution and those involved in the system, from the providers to the patients, carry little direct accountability for the consequences of their decisions.

I have lived through the era with the Presidential Fitness Awards in elementary school, where in gym class every year we would do sit-ups and pull-ups and shuttle runs in an effort to promote healthy living. But healthy living did not take hold. There was no incentive to continue. We are now having state governments ban salt and trans fats, we require fast food restaurants to display caloric and fat content, we are removing soda and vending machines from schools—but we still do not make individuals directly accountable for their lifestyle decisions. Until we do, we will not succeed in altering behavior.

The Massachusetts plan will not impact the growing obesity epidemic nor will it alter the pervading perception of health. A culture of health does not arise out of a top-down, government-mandated, authoritarian approach, especially in a free society. Change will come when individuals are properly incented to change behavior, where the goal of healthy living is expressed in the structure of the health care system, not when poor choices are covered by it.

For these reasons, the structure of the Massachusetts plan is fatally flawed, and as such, it should only exist as a side bar, a historical model from which we learn. It is a system whereby a few positives may be found to enhance an alternate approach, but as a platform upon which we can successfully transform our health care system—it miserably fails the application of an evidence-based approach. The outcome data speaks rather loudly for itself.

Health care consumerism, the alternate reform model, has its benefits and flaws. The CDHPs enacted in Indiana reduced costs both for the state and the employees. It has generated savings that if fully transferable (not likely, but interesting to consider) to our national health care expenditures would account for an additional $275 billion dollars in annual savings (11 percent of $2.5 trillion). This approach has improved the health risk in Indiana, and in Safeway (and Johnson&Johnson), this model not only improved the health of the employees but also brought about a decrease in workplace absenteeism, leading to secondary gains of improved productivity for the company and less salary loss for sick days for the employee. Unused contributions into the HSA are held by the beneficiary, and these funds can grow over time to act as a source of greater insurance against the impact of future illness—the employees in Indiana have demonstrated that this works.

Based upon the cost findings, it is a reform approach that is financially sustainable, and a model that reduces the shielding of the participants in the system from the costs of the system. And it is a system that can be used as that platform to construct a viable health care delivery system, one that can expand its effectiveness by further enhancing positive incentives through programs like Safeway's Healthy Measures. Incentives can be broadened to include financial reimbursement from insurance companies as well, for any improvement in health of their beneficiaries decreases their potential costs as well. It is a system that better aligns the participants in the system to focus on one thing— improving the overall health.

Flaws do exist within this model. Before moving on to the concerns, I want to first state again that I believe that any health care system needs to work for all members of society, not just the young, the wealthy, and the healthy. And therein lies most of the apprehension regarding this model. The ability of the working poor and their employer to place sufficient funds into an HSA so as to cover the high deductible can be difficult. The original RAND Hospital Insurance Experiment from the late 1970s did note that decreased cost sharing negatively impacted the health of the high health risk subset in the lower income strata. Other studies have demonstrated that even small co-pays can have a major adverse effect on lower income earners who as a result forego appropriate medical treatment or pass on the purchase of chronic medications present with more significant health issues. These patients end up utilizing high cost emergency rooms more often and require hospital admission that could have been prevented with proper medical care. For the chronically ill, greater cost sharing can lead to increased medical costs, as they become responsible for the higher deductible and higher out of pocket expenditures. And in a similar vein, since the chronically ill will more likely continue in the more comprehensive plans, less pooling of risk will occur as the healthier in society move to the CDHPs, and the cost of these plans will increase.

However, most of these studies were working within the context of the current system, not one that truly embraces the concept of heath care consumerism. The plans did not have the personal financial incentives of maintaining a lower cholesterol level, taking proper blood pressure medications, or controlling blood sugar levels, all components of the ideal associated with a smarter, patient-centered approach for the next generation of health care plans. Alternative designs continually adjust the workings of this fairly new model, one that came into existence within the last seven years. Most plans are now providing first dollar coverage for preventive medicine visits and cancer screenings. Some are shifting to cover medications for chronic illnesses. And an integral part of this model is patient education and transparency in all aspects of health and health care. Health coaches are being provided to assist participants to make better choices with regard to lifestyle management for the medical condition for which they are being treated. Robust quality and cost decision support tools are being developed and brought to the market. These can assist individuals to make more informed health choices with regard to the value of cost-effective therapies like generic medications. These products can help identify the most cost efficient providers as well as less expensive services like CT scans or physical therapy centers. Members are being encouraged to engage their physician in conversations about the value and alternatives regarding the treatment choices for their medical condition.

These processes in turn force physicians to become more aware of health care costs and make them more directly accountable to their patients for health care decisions. When the person sitting across from you, as opposed to that faceless entity of a third-party payer, carries a greater financial stake in your recommendations, the moral hazard of physician overutilization is suppressed. These approaches will grow and broaden as future generations of health care consumerism products come to the market.

For the poor and the sick, programs can be arranged to assist with coverage. But this is not to once again separate the patient from the cost of care or to lessen the potential of incentives. One source of possible funding to assist the poor is the government, especially if we see the level of cost savings as demonstrated in the state of Indiana and other large corporations that have adopted this approach. This assistance should be based upon payments into HSAs for healthy lifestyle choices like smoking cessation, weight management, and proper utilization of health care services (increased cost for non-emergent ER visits). I also believe that local charities, religious groups and individual donors should be able to provide tax-free dollars to support the growth of HSAs for the less fortunate as well. And for an important note, CDHP2, the Indiana model with less cost sharing, was found to have an actuarial value of .996 compared to the PPO. This means that this consumerism plan would cover 99.6 percent of the employee health care costs when compared to the comprehensive plan. And this consumerism-styled plan saved the state of Indiana 7.6 percent.

One final overriding concern often expressed about this approach is that while this sounds great, the members of our society are not able to learn, to change their habits regarding medicine, medical care and their health. I consider myself a realistic optimist, and I in no way maintain a pie in the sky view toward health care consumerism. Lifestyle choices and cultural norms are difficult to sway. I tell my patients regularly that they need to lose weight, exercise and eat better. Most continue to follow their well-established lifestyle patterns. But the data from Indiana and other corporations that instituted this approach shows that change is possible, that this approach does work, especially if we utilize the proper tools to motivate healthy behavior.

We cannot limit ourselves and toss aside effective reform out of fear that our society cannot adapt or grow or advance. We cannot limit ourselves to failed concepts purely out of lack of faith in humanity. Low expectations for society will not bring substantive progress. And change will not come from a top-down directive. Motivation for change needs to begin at the individual level—we just need to properly align the levers of incentives and minimize the moral hazard within the system to properly promote that change, to develop a culture of health.

The successes of health care consumerism are reality-based stories that demonstrate significant cost savings and positive alterations in health behavior. They are not hypothetical studies, or worse yet, the real life economic failure of the Massachusetts model. This is the type of model that demonstrates true efficacy in its ability to transform our health care system. Not ideology, not noise, just evidence.

THE PATIENT PROTECTION AND
AFFORDABLE CARE ACT

After discussing the volume of data and studies covered thus far, we have now reached the outcome of the national health care debate. This was the path chosen to cure the ills of our system; the approach to reform that will impact health care now and for coming generations. Those who have followed the thought process carried through this book hopefully have developed clarity about the ability of this legislation to resolve the structural issues impeding the development of an efficient, high-quality system.

President Barack Obama signed the Patient Protection and Affordable Care Act (PPACA) into law on March 23, 2010. On March, 31, 2010, the PPACA was amended by the Health Care and Education Reconciliation Act of 2010. This law was the outcome of the debates beginning in the spring of 2009 (really ongoing for decades), and those debates continue through today. The legislation is almost 2,500 pages of provisions, stipulations, enforcements, expansions, demonstrations, taxes, subsidies, pilots, requirements, mandates, regulations...The full breadth of its impact and the extent of its repercussions on our health care system and society at large will take years to thoroughly evaluate and understand.

But we do not have the leisure of time. The system will be fairly well entrenched before long. The law begins to slowly transform our health care system, with a few key provisions beginning this year and continuing in the subsequent years until 2014, at which time the major reforms commence. But if we wait, we may not be able to correct the course that has been set in motion.

Why the concern? Why the rush? The answer is fairly obvious. The PPACA is similar to the Massachusetts model, and that plan's impact on the state has brought more harm than good. And this plan, this law, makes the Massachusetts reform look conservative in its expansion of an unsound approach to the management of health care. If the PPACA follows the trajectory of the Massachusetts model, and there is little within the bill to think otherwise, then severe consequences will arise. I as a general rule disdain hyperbole and this level of concern is not coming from the perspective of a political ideologue. This conclusion is based on evidence.

Contrary to the Massachusetts plan, the PPACA has attempted, albeit modestly, to affect cost while also arranging demonstration projects and pilot programs as a means to search out further containment of expenditures. But in the end, all the PPACA did was add window dressings to a fundamentally flawed system as opposed to truly correcting the underlying structural issues, and this approach, based on evidence, will fail.

I am not going to discuss every aspect of the PPACA. I am not going to get lost in its breadth but will instead take a more global view. I am not here to discuss rationing, death panels, socialization of medicine, abortion, premiums in the individual market place versus group markets, or the constitutionality of mandates. I am not here to look at all of the specific impacts of the taxes or the new requirements on businesses and individuals and insurance companies and medical device manufacturers and the drug industry. I am here to evaluate the overarching themes rather than getting lost amongst the nuances of the legislation. I am here to present the forest from the trees.

Briefly, the structure matches the basics as laid out in Massachusetts. The expansion is just more pronounced. The PPACA establishes an individual and employer mandate; sets up insurance exchanges called the American Health Benefit Exchanges through which individuals and families up to 400 percent of the federal poverty level ($88,000 for a family of four) could receive federal subsidies to reduce the cost of purchasing insurance; expands the eligibility for Medicaid up to 133 percent of the federal poverty level; reduces Medicare payment rates for most services; imposes an excise tax on high premium plans, a.k.a. "Cadillac plans"; and increases taxation on participants within the system. In addition to this restructuring of the private health insurance market, the law sets minimum standards for health coverage, removes pre-existing conditions and prohibits lifetime benefits limits. And all the while, the federal government's control over the health care system grows.

I will relay information from the Congressional Budget Office (CBO), the Joint Committee on Taxation (JCT), and the Office of the Actuary of Centers for Medicare and Medicaid Services' (OA) evaluating the effects of the PPACA. These reports are readily found online. I will rarely extend the discussion into other evaluations of the law, instead focusing on the findings of these fiscal arbiters for our government. Their reports do carry a few important assumptions, including but not limited to:

1. Reform will be implemented exactly as stated in the law, with all cuts enacted despite their potential political detriment.
2. No successful legal challenges will alter any portion.
3. The law will not change human behavior—this specifically relates to the CBO and JCT.

Before moving into the reports from these entities, I want to provide some definitions of the expenditures that will be discussed. As mentioned previously, national health care expenditures are every single dollar spent on health care in the U.S., whether from the government, the private industry or individuals. Government health care expenditures are one component of our national expenditures and are those that specifically come from government spending on items within the PPACA that include but are not limited to Medicare, Medicaid, the additional exchange subsidies, and the development of new agencies or the expansion of old ones The federal budget is basically the government's checkbook—how much revenue comes in versus how much goes out. The impact on the federal deficit is purely whether government revenues exceed or fall short of expenditures. The understanding of these is important in order to grasp the impact of the legislation.

The CBO forecasts, which seem to carry most of the political fanfare, are limited to the impact of this reform on the federal budget. On the other hand, the OA projections cover both federal and overall national health care expenditures, a more practical and important view of the true impact of this plan on health care spending growth for our nation. And remember the goal as stated in the opening quote in the legislation: "The purpose of this is to provide affordable, quality health care for all Americans and reduce the growth in health care spending."

According to the latest CBO and JCT report from March 20, 2010, the cost of the bill has been estimated at $938 billion for years 2010-2019 with a few other discretionary items that bring the total package to around $1 trillion.[97] This expenditure is above and beyond the normal health care costs currently running about $2.5 trillion annually. And one point made by the OA: the revenue is collected beginning in 2010, whereas the real expenditures do not begin until 2014, so these figures represent 6 years of spending and 10 years of revenue collection. The analysis of the new legislation is therefore not a true 10 year accounting of cost.

Despite the additional cost of $1 trillion, the CBO estimates that the bill will yield a net reduction in the federal deficit of $148 billion over that ten year period. Sounds great. Even better, the bill is estimated to bring health insurance to an additional 32-34 million people, covering 94 percent of the nonelderly, legal U.S. population. And best yet, if you make less than 4 times the poverty level ($88,000 for a family of four), then you could get money from the government to help offset the cost of insurance if purchased through the exchanges (outside of employer-supported plans). The health insurance industry would have to accept all applicants (guaranteed issue) and children up to the age of 26 (they are children until 26 years old?) can stay on their parents' policy.

So we have a $1 trillion plan that covers more people, assists families with the cost of insurance, gets rid of those detestable insurance practices, and does all this while decreasing the federal deficit. Maybe that sounds too good to be true, especially in light of the previously presented data, but let's see what conclusion a more in-depth evaluation brings.

The CBO only comments on the effects of the bill on the federal budget, the government's checkbook. This means nothing to the personal budgets of American citizens. The cost problem is not a problem that only pertains to our government; it is a problem for our country. The government is just one participant in health care and only one segment of our society. Our total national health care expenditures are what really matter—these are the total costs of health care for our nation—for every man, woman, child and business. The ecstasy displayed around the CBO findings that this bill will decrease the deficit rings hollow if overall health care spending goes up. This is like the directors of the Massachusetts plan saying that the costs remain within their budgeted expectations while the people of Massachusetts struggle with rising health care costs, premium hikes, increased taxation, and economic suppression. So what has the law done with regard to the costs for our country as a whole?

The Chief Actuary for CMS (OA) has described the impact of this bill in that broader sense, the one that we as a country will feel. The report from April 22, 2010 states that "total national healthcare expenditures under this bill would increase by an estimated total of $311 billion."[98]So the PPACA has increased spending for our country, an increase that would not occur if we had maintained our current system. This plan does not correct the cost issues, it worsens them. It takes an unsustainable situation and accelerates its progress. It actually raises the cost curve. If we are worried about bankrupting our country, then why did we enact a plan that drives costs up? And how can our elected officials actually celebrate this costly piece of legislation that exacerbates that which it is supposed to correct? This makes no sense, no matter how it is couched or polished or presented.

Under the PPACA, the national health care expenditures are expected to rise to 21 percent of our GDP in 2019, reaching an estimated cost of $4.7 trillion. Despite implementing a $1 trillion piece of legislation that is supposed to fix our cost problem, we are still projecting the annual cost to rise from $2.5 trillion now to $4.7 in ten years. This corrects the unsustainable cost problem? Eventually, health care expenditures will crowd out other essential functions. We have put off truly fixing a problem and instead have passed it on the next generation, at which time the fix will be even more difficult and the damage perhaps irreparable.

I will move on from the travesty of rising national health care expenditures under the PPACA and view the bill from the eyes of the government's checkbook. This carries so much less significance in the scheme of reform but was the point so vociferously paraded to the public as carrying some type of real value. This was the noise that was meant to distract. That being said, reviewing this information does bring further insight into the workings of the bill.

So how does the CBO find that the PPACA decreases our federal deficit by $143 billion, especially when the report states that government spending on health care increases by over $400 billion? A better framework for the question may be—how does the government increase spending from one side of its ledger but still see a reduction in its overall deficit? How is this book being balanced? The answer is a combination of one of three ways. The spending can foster such strong changes in efficiency that costs come down. This would be like a printing company purchasing a new press. The initial outlay is substantial, but if the company can print greater volume at a cheaper rate, then its overall expenditures compared to revenues will decrease. The machine in essence pays for itself and then some. The other two answers are fairly straightforward—money can be taken from another side of the ledger through cuts in other programs or revenue can go up via increase in taxation.

Does the legislation pay for itself by increasing efficiency in the system? A number of proposals, most of which are small pilot programs, are included that seek out potential cost-saving measures. These range from bundling of payments to physicians, value-based purchasing, incentives for hospitals to reduce hospital-acquired conditions, pay-for-performance measures, fraud detection, and comparative effectiveness research. Some of these topics have been discussed in prior chapters. The CBO notes that the effects of these measures upon costs carry much uncertainty and their effects will take time to evaluate. It projects savings of about $14.1 billion (Table 5, TITLE III) but scores a majority of these programs as having no budget effect.[97]

This is a good time for a quick side step: unintended consequences too often are unaccounted for in legislation. More than half of the projected savings ($7.1 billion) come from decreased reimbursements to hospitals for patient readmissions within 30 days of discharge. This single change can potentially lead to longer inpatient hospital stays to minimize this risk, thus driving up cost, perhaps even more than if this were not included. Things seem so much better when we ignore those pesky unintended consequence.

The OA has also looked at these same measures and estimates "a relatively small reduction in non-Medicare federal health care expenditures of $2 billion for these provisions." So the plan does not make health care delivery more efficient. Quite the opposite—it falls short by about $998 billion. We may see gains down the line as these programs do carry potential benefit, but neither agency sees them significantly impacting the cost curve. This now puts us back to either cuts in other programs or increased taxation as a means to balance this $998 billion difference.

First the cuts. Medicare savings are expected to total $575 billion, of which $487 billion comes from cuts with the remaining difference attributed to increases in taxes. I will not delve too deeply into the cuts, but they are based mostly around decreasing reimbursement to hospitals, physicians, rehabilitation centers and other aspects of health care for our seniors.

The Medicare cuts will hold off the projected date of exhaustion of the trust fund by all of 12 years, moving the expected time from 2017 to 2029. I cannot personally understand the mindset where a $1 trillion bill is passed, $487 billion is cut from Medicare, and the supporters of the plan celebrate adding all of 12 additional years to the solvency of the Medicare Trust Fund. And then they have the audacity to trumpet the legislation as one that strengthens Medicare. What is supposed to happen in 12 years? That's not too far in the future. And what will be the effect of these cuts, this "strengthening of Medicare", upon our seniors in the interim?

The OA states that "providers for whom Medicare constitutes a substantive portion of their business could find it difficult to remain profitable and, absent legislative intervention, might end their participation in the program (possibly jeopardizing access to care for beneficiaries)." This concern regarding physicians withdrawing from Medicare was also echoed by the 2008 Medicare Payment Advisory Commission when it stated, "If Medicare rates were rapidly decreasing in relation to private sector rates, access for Medicare beneficiaries could become a concern."

According to a 2008 Milliman actuarial study, Medicare pays physicians at 78 percent of private insurance contracted rates, meaning that a physician gets paid 22 percent less to see a Medicare patient with the same health problem receiving the same level of care as a patient with private insurance.[99] As a result, approximately 74 percent of physicians take new Medicare patients compared to an 87 percent rate for private insurance. But overall access to health care for Medicare beneficiaries is currently comparable to the privately insured. However, anecdotal stories of physicians leaving the system are popping up in news reports daily.[100] With the looming payment cuts for provider services within the PPACA, these reports will become more common.

Unfortunately, the effects of the Medicare "savings" extend beyond physicians. "Simulations by the Office of the Actuary suggest that roughly 15 percent of Part A (hospital) providers would become unprofitable within the 10-year projection period." An unprofitable hospital, like an unprofitable business, cannot survive. Based upon the OA's evaluation of the impact of this legislation, hospitals will go out of business, fewer doctors will accept Medicare, and access to health care for seniors will worsen. And these are seniors who have paid into the system their entire lives. But $575 billion in Medicare cuts do not even begin to cover the entire cost of this plan. We still have substantial ground to cover to begin to turn this $1 trillion dollar legislation into a deficit reducer for the government's accounting.

So now come the taxes. Individual and business mandate penalties will collect $65 billion for the government. The excise tax on "Cadillac plans" will collect $32 billion. Taxation on medical device manufacturers (for example, those who make pacemakers), the pharmaceutical industry, and insurance industry are expected to raise $107 billion. The wage tax for Medicare will increase 0.9 percent on those with incomes exceeding $200,000 as an individual or $250,000 as a couple and will bring in $87 billion. For those at that same income level, a 3.8 percent Medicare tax will be instituted for the first time on investment income, including items like interest, dividends, rental income, etc. And take note, this tax is not indexed to inflation, so much like the Alternative Minimum Tax, a growing share of the population will be hit by it over time. This tax is expected to raise $123 billion. The total tax burden based on the CBO/JCT estimates from March 20, 2010: $520 billion.

These taxes will depress medical innovation. These taxes will stifle jobs. These taxes will impede economic growth. The economy is already struggling under the expectation of the coming tax burden. The folly of taxing people and businesses to this extent in the midst of a deep recession is fairly evident. I don't know many who believe that increasing taxation on businesses and individuals increases the availability of jobs and drives economic recovery. And those taxes on insurance companies, the pharmaceutical industry and others, according to the OA, will be "passed through to health consumers in the form of higher drug and device prices or higher insurance premiums."

The cost of this law that improves the government balance sheet is hoisted on the backs of a citizenry that can ill afford such reckless spending. Lest we forget, the goal of this bill was to make health care more reasonable, more affordable. It instead has created a boondoggle of escalating costs covered by swelling taxation and sweeping Medicare cuts. And in the end, it has raised the national health care expenditures by $311 billion and driven the cost curve upward. A blog on May 28, 2010 from Doug Elmendorf, the current director of the CBO, contained a rather succinct summary of the PPACA.[101]

"The central challenge is straightforward and stark: The rising costs of health care will put tremendous pressure on the federal budget during the next few decades and beyond. In CBO's judgment, the health legislation enacted earlier this year does not substantially diminish that pressure."

Like Mr. Elmendorf, I have yet to find any significant redeeming quality from this piece of legislation on the cost front. Yet the overall cost of the bill was broadcast for coming in below an arbitrary $1 trillion limit. Who picked that number, and how did it have any relevance to the point of the legislation? Noise. Who proclaimed the legislation as effective for taking $148 billion off the government's books—only to have done so by taking $575 billion from seniors and $520 billion from taxpaying citizens? More noise.

This is no different than me taking $5,000 from my neighbor to repave our cul de sac for $4,000, and then crowing to them about how wonderful it is that I have brought them a newly paved road while adding the extra $1,000 to my account. What would my neighbors say? What would you say? Yet these are the finances of health care reform that was sold to the American public. But there is more. At least my neighbors, in my brief example, have a newly paved road. We still have to see what value the PPACA has provided.

Before moving on to discuss the PPACA's impact on insurance coverage, I want to add one quick side note to demonstrate a budgeting gimmick used in the scoring of the legislation's cost. While I could cover quite a few others, it is beyond the scope of what I believe is necessary to demonstrate that this has occurred. And this point is made not to create additional angst but to make note that even after looking at the numbers above, the cost may actually be worse than presented.

As previously mentioned, the Medicare savings resulting from the cuts and new taxes extend the solvency of the Trust Fund. But based on government budget accounting rules (called unified budget accounting), the CBO also counted this revenue a second time in its calculations to reduce the federal deficit. This double counting, while it falls within the rules, rings hollow. The economics of this world are not based on CBO accounting rules. In reality, the savings can only be used once. As the OA states, "the improved HI [Medicare] financing cannot be simultaneously used to finance Federal outlays such as the coverage expansion and to extend the trust fund, despite the appearance of this result." This same conclusion was also drawn by the CBO, despite its continued use of this budgeting approach. In a letter to the Senate on January 22, 2010, the CBO stated, "Unified budget accounting shows that the majority of the HI trust fund savings under PPACA would be used to pay for other spending and therefore would not enhance the ability of the government to pay for future Medicare benefits."[102] Despite these statements, Kathleen Sebelius, the director for Health and Human Services, continues to espouse the double counting as appropriate.[103] Is there any wonder that new federal programs end up costing more in reality than projected in Congress?

So is there hope, a light in this darkness of rising health care costs, Medicare cuts and tax increases? This at least helps some people, at least brings access to quality care to those who need it most, right? Partly.

The expansion of health insurance to 34 million people sounds great… until we look just a little below the surface. A large portion (16-18 million) will come from the expansion of Medicaid. The issue: only 50 percent of physicians take Medicaid. Anecdotally, I know of only two private practice urologists in Atlanta who do. Why? Medicaid reimburses at 53 percent of the private insurance rate—it does not pay enough to even cover the cost of delivering care. And once again, based upon the changes in the PPACA, the OA states that "providers might tend to accept more patients who have private insurance and fewer Medicare and Medicaid patients, exacerbating existing access problems for the latter group...[an] outcome [that] should be considered plausible and even probable." So we have basically put our health care system and our society through this maelstrom of change and financial hazard to bring really bad insurance to more than half of the newly covered population. One would hope that we could do better.

The problems regarding Medicaid expansion extend beyond the access problems for those patients. According to the Kaiser Commission on Medicaid and the Uninsured, state spending on Medicaid would increase $21.1 to $43 billion during the years 2014-2019, depending upon the how aggressively participation is pursued.[104] The initial cost to the state for the expansion of Medicaid for newly eligible participants is covered 100 percent by the federal government. However, that expense progressively moves to the state as the federal government's coverage falls to 93 percent by 2019 and to 90 percent thereafter. If this sounds familiar, it is. This is the same approach that got people into trouble when they purchased homes on an adjustable rate mortgage. While the mortgages were affordable early on, as the interest rate rose, the cost escalated.

By 2019 in Georgia, using the conservative estimates, Medicaid enrollment is expected to increase 40.4 percent, costing the state $714 million over those 6 years. Using the more aggressive enrollment scenario, the numbers point to a 56.7 percent increase in Medicaid at a cost of $1.233 billion. Does this make sense when the federal government just had to send $26 billion to the states to pay for current Medicaid funding shortfalls and help plug holes in state budgets? In Georgia, we are furloughing teachers, decreasing the numbers of firemen and policemen, laying off state workers and limiting our legal system because of budget shortfalls. The states cannot tolerate these increased costs. More layoffs will have to ensue, or taxes will have to dramatically rise at the state level. In expanding the Medicaid program, we are giving people health insurance that does not equate with access to health care, and we are doing it at the expense of our nation's economic well-being.

To now recap with a broader understanding: we have a $1 trillion dollar plan that expands healthcare to 33-34 million people. It raises the costs of what is already considered an unsustainable cost problem by $311 billion more than if we kept the current system. It cuts access to health care for our seniors and collects over $520 billion in taxes. A majority of those who obtain health insurance receive a substandard product (Medicaid) that few physicians will take. Our states will have to find more cuts or raise taxes or both to cover their additional costs. Medicare still goes bankrupt, just 12 years later. And in this economic environment, the economy will continue to struggle, jobs will be scarce, unemployment will persist…oh, and I have yet to address the possibility that this reform may drive current physicians to retire early or make future physicians less inclined to pursue a medical career, further worsening a physician shortage already expected to leave us short of 200,000 doctors by 2020.

All is not well with this picture. The data from studies and the evaluation of Massachusetts, the template for the PPACA, fully supports these concerns. I will once again reiterate the overriding theme throughout this book: no matter how benevolent, how hopeful, how caring or how well-intended plans may be, if they are not rooted in the reality of the economics of our world, then they will fail. And in doing so, good will not come. Only harm will follow. And the Hippocratic Oath, in its simplest statement simply states: "Do no harm." Whatever happened to a little common sense, a little honest evaluation, and a little more truthfulness? How about a little less ideology and a lot more evidence.

Conclusion

So this is what I looked at, this is what I read, and this is my commentary developed out of the research. I have tried to avoid misrepresenting data. I see no place for rhetoric, much less ideologically-driven misinformation or statistical manipulation. Policy that delivers positive gains for our society can only come about through honest, forthright and transparent identification of the problems and their solutions. I hope I have met this standard. I have referenced everything, so please do not take my word or accept my analysis without discernment or question. We as a society have often been lead astray because we accept others' points of view without challenging the information that supports that view.

I have written this book to present data, to reevaluate the reform choices and to hopefully begin the process of developing a more effective alternative for the future of our health care delivery system. The Patient Protection and Affordable Care Act falls woefully short of achieving the proper transformation so desperately needed, and unless we change our approach, we will never reach the goal of creating a high-quality, readily-accessible, cost-efficient health care system for our nation.

I am not exerting that any contradictory thought is erroneous. Only a fool would believe that he is the sole possessor of knowledge and truth. Medicine has taught me humility: While science and data and historical context help direct us toward proper diagnoses and treatments, medicine still carries an artful side, a gestalt. But if we ignore evidence and follow emotion and ideology, then the risk of an incorrect decision swells, and healing, whether it is the health care system or a patient in my office, is less likely. It is the science applied properly and honestly that enhances our chance of success.

My goal extends beyond reviewing the health care reform process from an evidence-based approach. I also hope to provide a fresh perspective on a better method to solve the bevy of issues we face outside of medicine. I am well aware that this is not a new concept—I just do not see it being practiced by those leading our country. And this is in no way specific to one party.

I hope that we as a society will reassess our political process. So much noise exists within the currently accepted practice of government, and issues are not being resolved. We continue to dig a deeper hole. We are not progressing. And societies that do not progress, that stagnate, inevitably fall behind. But I believe that if we remove the noise of politics as it is currently practiced and begin to hold our elected officials to a higher standard, if we focus on more data-driven solutions uninhibited by the ideology of the extremes, then we may actually be able to develop a society where social, spiritual, fiscal, and personal prosperity reigns.

If this is our goal, the view that we hold for our future, then I want to pause. The following is as self-indicting as it is a call to fellow citizens, so please do not read this without understanding that it comes from a place of ongoing self evaluation. I want to propose that we silence our own preconceived notions; that we think for a moment without that inner noise of ideology that is all too often destructive, divisive and confounding. We continuously hear politicians, columnists, radio hosts, news media and political talking heads berate one party or the other. Blog posts and organizations spew venom and paint radical pictures of our fellow citizens. Republicans are labeled as the party of big business; the party of the wealthy; the party that does not care for the poor, the underprivileged, the hungry; the party of war. The Democrats are labeled as socialists, the party of taxation, the party of entitlement, the environmentalists. If your neighbor is a Republican, does that really mean that he or she is heartless with little sympathy or desire to help those in need? And if your neighbor is a Democrat, does that really mean that he or she is a socialist who espouses taxing and spending and the destruction of a free market society? Is it really that simple to divide our brothers and sisters, our fellow citizens, and paint them with such a broad brush stroke?

More can be gained through unification than division. Divisiveness is used to weaken, to conquer, and to oppress. Approaching governing in this manner leads to winners and losers—it is a game that hinges on leaders controlling the perception of the members of society, separating them into fragmented groups with opposing goals, a populace that can more easily be manipulated to bring about a set political agenda. Any victory occurs at the expense of others, and the ties that bind society weaken further. On the other hand, unification can strengthen a society and bring about a singular vision founded upon shared goals. Finding that commonality of purpose, that underlying inherent good that unifies our society, will focus political energy on solutions that lead to the betterment of all citizens. This is the value of unity of purpose, and in this model of governance, more celebrate the victory of legislative achievement, and the nation grows stronger.

To reach this end, we must move beyond the limitations of these labels that promote marginalization and debasement. Our society has seen the destruction associated with viewing others through the narrowed lens of prejudice, yet it remains accepted and even encouraged in the interplay of politics. Our conversations no longer embrace the robust exchange of ideas that foster the enactment of policy that builds the foundation for a stronger society. Instead, we often reject contrary thought without evaluating its veracity and its potential to bring about value for this world. Such divisiveness clouds judgment and inhibits the necessary dialogue that must be undertaken to openly and honestly identify problems and solutions.

So if we take a moment and consider what we want to see within our society, do our goals really vary from one person to another, irrespective of the labels we place upon each other? It may be that the time has come to deconstruct our political views, to silence the noise associated with what we have established as our ideology and get back to the essence of our personal beliefs.

The next two paragraphs express my beliefs regarding society in the first person. I do not want to misappropriate pronouns and create false supposition, transposing what I believe to be a common set of desires for our society onto others. I would rather allow those who read this to determine whether my "I" matches their "I". All are not going to agree with every thought, every sentence. These are my views, and none of us accept in whole the individual parts of other's ideals. But we can agree with the sum, the overarching concepts, and I believe that most of us do carry a similar thread with regards to the view of our society, of this world and the future that we want to see unfold.

I believe that we all want to be fulfilled. And I believe that we all want our fellow brothers and sisters within this society to reach a level of well-being as well. Its attainment is not based solely upon accumulation of wealth, physical health, power, success, or even happiness, for each individual differently defines that which brings them a higher level of contentedness in life. But I believe that our society should be one that provides the liberty to pursue the attainment of personal well-being, where the opportunity to thrive and maximize our potential exists unencumbered by external forces such as poverty, greed, corruption, racism, and the tyranny of government and men.

I believe that if we gathered people from all walks of life, we will find a common thread in the hope that we can develop a society where tomorrow, we will be better than today; where tomorrow, we have progressed—more people are working, more people are receiving high-quality education, more people have access to health care and food and housing and opportunity. I believe in the vision of a tomorrow where our environment is cleaner, where the world is safer, and where we help struggling nations advance and develop. A tomorrow where the next generation is left a more fruitful world than the previous is not some unattainable goal, some fanciful view of the future. I truly believe that it is possible.

But in order to fulfill the potential of our society, we as citizens must individually evaluate our personal beliefs and then collectively decide the "what" that we want to achieve. We need to set the goals for our nation based on a shared purpose. So what are some of these possible endpoints that arise out of our belief system, this "what" that we are looking to resolve? The book covered the development of a more efficient health care system that provides greater access at less expense. Goals may also include an educational system that minimizes disparity in test scores amongst socioeconomic groups and allows our children to keep pace with and exceed other competing nations; a fiscal system that properly balances risk and reward to best achieve prosperity and avoid economic collapse; a governmental system where the public sector, taxation and spending do not constrain the ability of the private sector to bring about national prosperity; a social safety net for the poor that restores the hope of a better tomorrow while minimizing the hazards of entitlement and dependence that destroy the human spirit and lead to the development of intergenerational poverty.

Once we have outlined our "what", then we can then progress to determine the "how." Having goals is necessary, but having a plan is an equal, if not more important, task. Goals that are not built on a sustainable, effective plan will fail. Plans built on hopes and dreams and fanciful wishes and political ideology without a basis in the reality of finances, of human nature and of plain old common sense will fail. And yet much of the political speeches, television reports and news stories regarding the choices that our elected officials are making on behalf of our society, on behalf of you and me, provide little of substance or truthfulness. They focus instead on emotion and sensationalism, eschewing honest evaluation of the substance of policy for political gain or self interest. Demagoguery and obfuscation are the norm, not candid and open debate.

Politics has become a game of deception, a ruse where the outcome of policy means less than the policy-making itself. But if we step back from the chicanery that is the current practice of politics, we will realize that it is the outcome that truly matters. For example, if we pass fiscal and social policy aimed to increase work force participation amongst the inner city population that leads to an increase in unemployment, then no one wins. Self congratulating for the achievement of making a law that exacerbates that which it has claimed to correct rings hollow, and such an act is no more humane than ignoring the problem in the first place.

But any change in this political approach has to come from citizens. We have to demand that our legislators develop policy that is not based on the whimsical nature of those in power but rather follows the directive of evidence and data. This means that we have to extend ourselves beyond the sound bites, the speeches and the pomp and circumstance of politics. The time where we choose our politics based upon race or social status has to end. The time where we inherit our politics from our parents, our teachers, or our friends has to end. The time where we choose our elected officials based on how well they dress, make us feel or give a speech has to end. We need thinkers and problem-solvers. And we have to make an effort to avoid being swayed by those who prefer to marginalize rather than invoke debate, those who dispel ideas based on half-truths and emotion rather than fact and substance. We individually must evaluate our own belief structure, to choose the "what" that we want to see accomplished, and then determine whether the "how" as laid out by our legislators truly meets that end.

We have strayed from a path that leads to corrective solutions, and while I do not believe in speaking in hyperbole, time is short. We are rapidly heading toward a tipping point. For if we do not properly identify the problems and choose the appropriate approach to solve those problems, then our society will become another footnote in history, nothing more than a brave attempt at freedom, liberty and self-determination. I hope the small amount of knowledge that I have been able to ascertain brings power and certainty and strength and determination to those who read this book. I truly hope this helps, for I am not ready to concede.

Notes

1. http://www.cms.hhs.gov/NationalHealthExpendData/03_NationalHealthAccoun tsProjected.asp#TopOfPage
2. http://www.cms.gov/NationalHealthExpendData/downloads/NHE_Extended_Pr ojections.pdf
3. http://www.socialsecurity.gov/OACT/TRSUM/tr09summary.pdf
4. http://www.kff.org/medicare/upload/7305-04-2.pdf
5. http://data.bls.gov/cgi-bin/surveymost
6. http://ehbs.kff.org/pdf/2009/7937.pdf
7. http://www.newamerica.net/files/nafmigration/Employer_Burden_issue_brief.p df
8. http://www.nber.org/papers/w3163.pdf
9. http://www.amjmed.com/article/S0002-9343(09)00404-5/abstract
10. http://www.narprail.org/cms/images/uploads/fund.pdf
11. http://www.thedailybeast.com/blogs-and-stories/2010-07-29/peter-orszags-parting-shots-obamas-budget-chief-exits/2/
12. Jeffrey H. Anderson, "Medicare's Costs Have Risen Far More Than the Costs of Private Health Care," *Health Policy Prescriptions, Vol. 7, No. 06* (June 2009).
13. http://liberty.pacificresearch.org/docLib/20090714_HPPv7n07_0709.pdf
14. https://www.cms.gov/NationalHealthExpendData/downloads/2004-age-tables.pdf
15. http://www.heritage.org/Research/Reports/2009/07/Illusions-of-Cost-Control-in-Public-Health-Care-Plans
16. http://institute.ourfuture.org/files/Jacob_Hacker_Public_Plan_Choice.pdf
17. "Follow-Up Memorandum to the Distribution of Total Expenses by Source of Payments for Two Groups," technical memorandum to the Joint Economic Committee, May 22, 2003
18. http://medpac.gov/documents/Jun08DataBook_Entire_report.pdf
19. http://voices.washingtonpost.com/ezra-klein/2009/07/administrative_costs_in_health.html
20. http://www.ama-assn.org/ama1/pub/upload/mm/478/admincosts.pdf
21. http://www.manhattan-institute.org/html/mpr_05.htm
22. http://www.heritage.org/Research/Reports/2009/06/Medicare-Administrative-Costs-Are-Higher-Not-Lower-Than-for-Private-Insurance
23. Litow, Mark E., "Medicare versus Private Health Insurance: The Cost of Administration," Milliman, January 6, 2006.
24. http://www.bus.umich.edu/otpr/WP2007-1.pdf
25. Feldstein, Martin. 2006. The effects of taxes on efficiency and growth. NBER Working PaperNo. 12201.
26. "Rhetoric vs. Reality: Comparing Public and Private Health Care Costs," Mark Litow and CAHI's Technical Committee, Council for Affordable Health Insurance, 1994.
27. http://www.cbo.gov/ftpdocs/99xx/doc9924/Chapter3.7.1.shtml
28. http://content.healthaffairs.org/cgi/content/abstract/29/6/1248

29. http://content.healthaffairs.org/cgi/content/abstract/28/4/w544
30. http://content.healthaffairs.org/cgi/content/abstract/28/4/w533

31. http://content.healthaffairs.org/cgi/content/full/24/6/1629
32. http://www.nejm.org/doi/full/10.1056/NEJMsa022033?keytype2=tf_ipsecsha&ij
    key=53a7db2ac819a101e641be48832ade6e481cc4b0#articleDiscussion
33. http://jop.ascopubs.org/content/5/6/291.full#sec-9
34. Woolhandler S, Himmelstein DU. The deteriorating administrative efficiency of
    the U.S. health care system. N Engl J Med 1991; 324:1253-8.
35. http://www.pnhp.org/publications/nejmadmin.pdf
36. http://content.healthaffairs.org/cgi/reprint/11/1/21.pdf
37. http://economix.blogs.nytimes.com/2008/11/21/why-does-us-health-care-cost-
    so-much-part-ii-indefensible-administrative-costs/
38. http://hcfan.3cdn.net/a9ce29d3038ef8a1e1_dhm6b9q0l.pdf
39. http://washingtonindependent.com/55535/tort-reform-unlikely-to-cut-health-
    care-costs
40. http://insight.kellogg.northwestern.edu/index.php/Kellogg/article/tort_reform_n
    o_miracle_cure
41. http://www.youtube.com/watch?v=N9HcWd5ifBA
42. http://www.oecd.org/document/16/0,3343,en_2649_34631_2085200_1_1_1_1
    ,00.html
43. K.E. Thorpe et al., "The Impact of Obesity on Rising Medical Spending,"
    Health Affairs 23 (2004): w480–w486 (published online 20 October 2004;
    10.1377/hlthaff.w4.480)
44. http://content.healthaffairs.org/cgi/content/short/hlthaff.28.5.w822
45. http://content.healthaffairs.org/cgi/content/short/hlthaff.28.5.w822
46. http://blogs.wsj.com/economics/2009/07/27/does-health-insurance-make-you-
    fat/
47. http://www.nber.org/papers/w15163
48. http://www.ers.usda.gov/publications/efan04004/efan04004g.pdf
49. Ehrlich I, Becker G. 1972. "Market Insurance, Self-Insurance, and Self-
    Protection." The Journal of Political Economy, 80(4), pp. 623-648.
50. http://www.docstoc.com/docs/12166952/Ezekiel-J-Emanuel-The-Perfect-
    Storm-of-Overutilization
51. http://www.kff.org/insurance/upload/7852.pdf
52. http://www.commonwealthfund.org/~/media/Files/Publications/Issue%20Brief/
    2005/Apr/The%20Effect%20of%20Health%20Savings%20Accounts%20on%
    20Health%20Insurance%20Coverage/811_Glied_effect_hlt_savings_account
    s_coverage%20pdf.pdf
53. http://www.commonwealthfund.org/~/media/Files/Publications/Testimony/2006
    /Sep/Health%20Savings%20Accounts%20and%20High%20Deductible%20H
    ealth%20Plans%20%20Why%20They%20Wont%20Cure%20What%20Ails%
    20U%20S%20%20Health%20C/957_Collins_SenateFinance_Testimony_09
    %2025%2006%20pdf.pdf
54. http://www.kff.org/uninsured/upload/7568.pdf
55. http://www.rand.org/pubs/research_briefs/RB9174/index1.html
56. http://www.kff.org/insurance/upload/7566.pdf
57. http://www.actuary.org/pdf/health/cdhp_may09.pdf
58. http://www.aetna.com/news/newsReleases/2009/0310_AHF_Results.html
59. http://www.med.upenn.edu/ldichi/docs/issue_brief_feb_091.pdf
60. http://www.newyorker.com/archive/2005/08/29/050829fa_fact?currentPage=all
    #ixzz0tcTDoxsN
61. http://www.mathematica-
    mpr.com/publications/PDFs/Health/reformhealthcare_IB5.pdf

62. http://www.cdc.gov/cancer/lung/basic_info/risk_factors.htm
63. Klick, Jonathan and Stratmann, Thomas, Diabetes Treatments and Moral Hazard. Journal of Law and Economics, Vol. 50, p. 519, 2007; FSU College of Law, Law and Economics Paper No. 05-21; FSU College of Law, Public Law Research Paper No. 159. Available at SSRN: http://ssrn.com/abstract=766825
64. http://www.palgrave-journals.com/gpp/journal/v33/n4/pdf/gpp200827a.pdf
65. http://www.cbo.gov/ftpdocs/87xx/doc8758/11-13-LT-Health.pdf
66. http://www.med.upenn.edu/ldichi/docs/issue_brief_feb_091.pdf
67. http://content.nejm.org/cgi/content/full/360/7/699
68. http://online.wsj.com/article/SB124476804026308603.html
69. http://articles.sfgate.com/2009-06-14/business/17209808_1_steve-burd-safeway-senior-vice-president-health-care
70. http://online.wsj.com/article/SB124536722522229323.html
71. http://www.cnsnews.com/news/article/52318
72. https://www.businessgrouphealth.org/meetings/forum2007/presentations/thursdaywatsonwyatt_survey.pdf
73. http://www.uswwa.org/portal/uswwa/case/default
74. http://www.hewittassociates.com/_MetaBasicCMAssetCache_/Assets/Articles/2009/BRT_Hewitt_HC_Reform_Report_Nov2009.pdf
75. http://www.bcbs.com/blueresources/mcrg/chapter5/ch5_slide_4.html
76. http://roomfordebate.blogs.nytimes.com/2010/06/14/should-people-be-paid-to-stay-healthy/
77. Jerry Cromwell "Cost savings and physician responses to global bundled payments for Medicare heart bypass surgery - Innovations in Fee-For-Service Financing and Delivery".
78. Casale A, Paulus RA, Selna MJ, Doll MC, Bothe AE Jr, McKinley KE, Berry SA, Davis DE, Gilfillan RJ, Hamory BH, Steele GD Jr, "'ProvenCareSM': A Provider-Driven Pay-for-Performance Program for Acute Episodic Cardiac Surgical Care," Annals of Surgery, Vol. 246, No. 4, October 2007, pp. 613–621.
79. http://www.healthtransformation.net/galleries/wpconsumerism/Healthcare%20Consumer-ism%20%20The%20Basis%20of%20a%2021st%20Century%20Intelligent%20Health%20System.pdf
80. http://www.mass.gov/Eeohhs2/docs/dhcfp/cost_trend_docs/final_report_docs/health_care_cost_trends_2010_final_report.pdf
81. http://publichealth.blog.state.ma.us/2010/02/release-of-health-care-cost-trends-reports.html
82. http://www.rand.org/pubs/research_briefs/RB9464-1/index1.html
83. "Massachusetts Healthcare Reform" (Power-Point Presentation, Office of the Governor, April10, 2006).
84. "Health Benefits Survey 2007," United BenefitsAdvisors, http://www.bio-medicine.org/medicinenews-1/survey-3a-massachusetts-employers—employees-paying-most-for-health-care-plans-10689-2/. John McDonough, "Massachusetts Health ReformImplementation: Major Progress and Future-Challenges," Health Affairs (June 3, 2008): w285–97."2009 CommCare Premium Contributions and Affordability Schedules," March12, 2009 http://mahealthconnector.org/portal/binary/com.epicentric.contentmanagement.servlet.ContentDeliveryServlet/About%2520Us/Publications%2520and%2520Reports/Current/Connector%2520Board%2520Meeting%2520March%2520

12%252C%25202009/Affordability%2520Schedule%25202009%2520%2528 3-11-09%2520revised_2%2529.ppt#257,1,Slide 1

85. "Survey of Employer Health Benefits 2007,"Kaiser Family Foundation, http://www.kff.org/insurance/7672/upload/7693.pdf.; "Survey of Employer-Health Benefits 2008," Kaiser Family Foundation, http://ehbs.kff.org/images/abstract/7814.pdf.; "Hewitt Data Reveals Little Change in U.S. Health Care Cost Increases for 2009," HewittAssociates LLC, http://www.hewittassociates.com/Intl/NA/enUS/AboutHewitt/Newsroom/Press ReleaseDetail.aspx?cid=5604.

86. John F. Cogan, R. Glenn Hubbard, and Daniel Kessler (2010) "The Effect of Massachusetts' Health Reform on Employer-Sponsored Insurance Premiums," *Forum for Health Economics & Policy*: Vol. 13: Iss. 2 (Health CareReform),Article 5.
http://www.bepress.com/fhep/13/2/5

87. http://www.mass.gov/Eeohhs2/docs/dhcfp/r/cost_trends_files/part2_premium_l evels_and_trends.pdf

88. http://www.nytimes.com/2009/07/15/us/15insure.html?_r=1

89. http://www.boston.com/news/local/massachusetts/articles/2009/06/24/state_cu ts_its_health_coverage_by_115m/

90. "2009 Survey of Physician Appointment Wait Times," www.merritthawkins.com

91. http://www.mass.gov/Eeohhs2/docs/dhcfp/r/pubs/10/barriers_policy_brief_201 0_05.pdf

92. http://www.mass.gov/?pageID=eohhs2terminal&L=4&L0=Home&L1=Research er&L2=Physical+Health+and+Treatment&L3=Health+Care+Delivery+System &sid=Eeohhs2&b=terminalcontent&f=dhcfp_researcher_all_dhcfp_publication s&csid=Eeohhs2\#primary_care

93. http://www.masslive.com/news/index.ssf/2010/03/mass-type_health_care_could_wi.html

94. http://www.pnhp.org/mass_report/mass_report_Final.pdf

95. http://www.heartland.org/full/26302/Indiana_HSA_Success_a_Lesson_for_Oth er_States.html

96. http://www.kff.org/healthreform/upload/7946.pdf

97. http://www.cbo.gov/ftpdocs/113xx/doc11379/AmendReconProp.pdf

98. http://burgess.house.gov/UploadedFiles/4-22-2010_-_OACT_Memorandum_on_Financial_Impact_of_PPACA_as_Enacted.pdf

99. Milliman, "Hospital and Physician Cost Shift Payment Level Comparison of Medicare, Medicaid, and Commercial Payers," December, 2008

100. http://www.nytimes.com/2009/04/02/business/retirementspecial/02health.html

101. http://cboblog.cbo.gov/?cat=5

102. http://www.cbo.gov/ftpdocs/110xx/doc11005/01-22-HI_Fund.pdf

103. http://spectator.org/blog/2010/08/02/sebelius-makes-false-claim-abo

104. http://www.kff.org/healthreform/upload/Medicaid-Coverage-and-Spending-in-Health-Reform-National-and-State-By-State-Results-for-Adults-at-or-Below-133-FPL-Executive-Summary.pdf

Schedule Dr. Brian E. Hill

Dr. Hill has appeared on both radio and TV and frequently travels for speaking engagements to medical, civic and professional groups.

To schedule Dr. Hill for your meeting, conference, or other event, please email:

stopthenoisehealthcare@gmail.com

LaVergne, TN USA
22 October 2010
201893LV00001BA/1/P